Linda & Mike, hope you enjoy it!
Love Susan xxx

A Beginner's Guide to

Ireland's Seashore

Helena Challinor

Susan Murphy Wickens

Jane Clark

Audrey Murphy

PHOTOGRAPHY BY

Paul Kay

Terry

A Sherkin Island Ma

Published by Sherkin Island Marine Station

ISBN: 1 870492 96 X

Design & layout: Susan Murphy Wickens

Drawings by: Audrey Murphy

Printed by: City Print Ltd., Victoria Cross, Cork, Ireland.

Photographs

Paul Kay: Cover photo, pages 1, 6, 8, 10, 16, 18, 19a, 19b, 20, 22, 23, 25, 32, 38a, 41, 42, 43, 44, 45a, 48a, 48b, 57, 58, 59, 60, 62, 63, 64, 65, 66, 68, 71, 72, 73, 74, 75, 76, 80a, 80b, 81, 82, 83, 84, 85, 86, 87, 88, 89, 90, 91, 92, 96, 97, 98, 100, 101, 102, 103, 104, 105, 106, 112, 115, 116a, 116b, 117, 121, 122, 123, 124, 126, 127, 129, 130, 131, 132, 139, 140, 142, 143, 144, 145, 146, 147, 148, 149, 150, 151, 152, 155, 156, 157, 158, 159, 160, 161, 162, 163, 164, 165, 166, 167, 168, 171, 172, 173, 174, 176, 177a, 177b, 178, 179, 181, 182, 183, 184, 185, 186a, 186b, 187a, 187b, 188, 189.

Terry Farnell: pages 7, 21, 26, 37, 38b, 39, 40, 45b, 46, 47, 49, 50, 51, 52, 53a, 53b, 54, 55a, 55b, 56, 67a, 67b, 99, 113, 114, 118, 119, 120, 125, 128, 138, 141, 175, 180.

Special thanks to the following for proof-reading, helpful criticism and encouragment: John Akeroyd, Jenny Baker, Gillian Bishop, Michael & Noeleen Courtney, Edward Fahy, Terry Farnell, Katie Gillham, Mike Guiry, John Joyce, Michael Ludwig, Richard McKeone, Robbie Murphy, Nuala Norris, Amy Norris, Liam O'Regan, Geoffery O'Sullivan, Chris Spurrier, Shirley Stone, Tony Walker.

The reference used for scientific names contained in this guide was "The Species Directory of the Marine Fauna and Flora of the British Isles and Surround Seas", produced by the Ulster Museum and Marine Conservation Society. Eds. Howson & Picton, 1997. ISBN 0 948150 06 8

Cover photo: Richard McKeone, Audrey Murphy, Amy Norris

This book is dedicated to the memory of Anthony Tower and his love of Ireland.

Anthony was taught to fish at an early age by his father on the beaches of Sussex, England. His horizons were broadened by his discovery of Ireland in the 1980's. It was here he developed a love of the beaches and people of West Cork. It was also where his love of fishing was confirmed when in September 1984 he caught a 10lb bass from the beaches at Rosscarbery, for which he was given an award by the Irish Fisheries Board.

It is hoped that through this book you will discover the joys of the natural world of Ireland. Perhaps you will teach your father how to fish!

"Oh, the beautiful shores of the West Coast of Cork

Are calling forever to me,

From the high hill o'er Schull and the Carbery islands

To the Fastnet way out in the sea,

To climb to the top of Brow Head on Sunday,

See the sea birds nestle and glide.

To stand with a rod on the shores of West Cork

And wait for the fish on the tide......."

'The Shores of West Cork' by J.A. Quish

ACKNOWLEDGEMENTS

Many tides have come and gone from the shores of Sherkin Island since my late wife Eileen and I discussed the compilation of a simple guide to the Irish seashore for beginners. We made many attempts to produce such a book, but lack of finance was always a problem. Then some years ago I had a visit at the marine station from Mrs. Barbara Ann Tower. She wanted to fund a project that would be a lasting tribute to her late husband, Tony. I immediately suggested "A Beginner's Guide to Ireland's Seashore" and happily Barbara agreed with the idea. Her generosity has made this book possible.

I was delighted when one of the marine station's former biologists, Helena Challinor, agreed to write it. She was ideally suited, as she has a wonderful ability to communicate with children. Working alongside Helena was my daughter, Susan, who was determined to produce something beginners would truly understand. She bore the challenge of designing and editing the book, encouraging everyone to contribute, especially Jane Clark, a volunteer biologist at the marine station, and my youngest daughter, Audrey.

I want to thank Paul Kay, who began his marine photography career at Sherkin Island in the early 1980s. His wonderful talent has brought the seashore to life in this book. Thanks are due, too, to Terry Farnell, also a former biologist at the station, for contributing photographs and for his advice and help with the book. Thank you to the members of An Buanchoiste Téarmaíochta (The Permanent Terminology Committee of the Department of Education), particularly Fidelma Ní Ghallchobhair, for their wonderful assistance with the Irish names.

Thanks to our printers, the Courtney family at City Print, Cork, for their generosity and wonderful help over the years. And last, but not least, our gratitude also to the many others who have helped with proof-reading, comments and feedback; in fact, to all who have helped make this book what it is.

Matt Murphy

CONTENTS

Page No.

INTRODUCTION

When we think of a seashore, we usually imagine golden sandy beaches, but the seashores around Ireland are far more varied than that. They range from sand to shingle, from smelly mudflats to razor sharp rocks. The animals and plants living there are even more varied, though it may take more than a quick look to find them. We hope this book will help you find and identify some of these creatures.

The book has been divided into three sections. The first part gives you general information on the seashore, and the various living conditions of animals and plants on different shores. This section will also tell you how to prepare for a trip to the shore. The seashore can be a dangerous place and can also be easily damaged, if you are not careful.

In the second part of the book, the information and diagrams of animals and plants in each group, together with photographs, will help you identify some of the specimens you might find on the shore.

At the end of the book (in the glossary), some of the more unusual but important words are explained. These words are in **bold** type throughout the book. There is also a list of other books you might like to read, as well as an index of all the animals and plants in the guide.

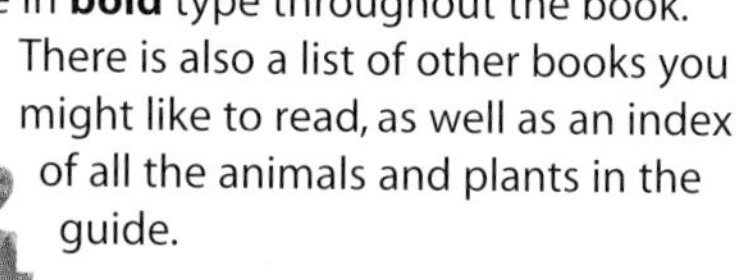

How to Use This Book

Animals, as well as plants, are divided into different groups. Those which have similar characteristics are grouped together. Just as domestic cats and tigers are included under the "family" heading of "cats", so too all other animals and plants are grouped in "families". This system of grouping animals and plants with similar characteristics is called **classification**. Although the groups on the seashore also have scientific names, in some cases we have used simpler ones. These are listed on page 9 and are colour-coded to make it easier to find them in the book.

There is an introduction to each group, giving you important information. Then, for each animal and plant included in the book, there is a photograph and a description, to help you identify them. Remember, words in **bold** type are listed in the glossary at the back of the book.

But perhaps you do not know to which group your specimen belongs. If you have found something that you want to identify, you first need to decide whether it is plant or animal. Be careful, there are many animals on the shore that look like plants, so it is not as easy as you might think. There is a simple guide on page 10 to help you. Sometimes you might find only part of an animal or plant and this can be misleading. Check under other group headings if you do not find what you are looking for in the first one.

Here is a sample page, showing you a typical layout.

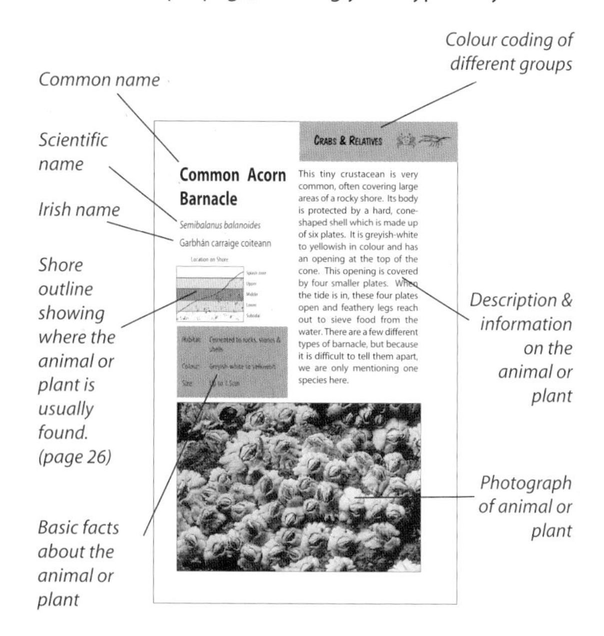

Note: Some animals and plants do not have Common or Irish names. For more information on **scientific names** see the glossary on page 195.

Plant & Animal Groups

The Plants

The Animals

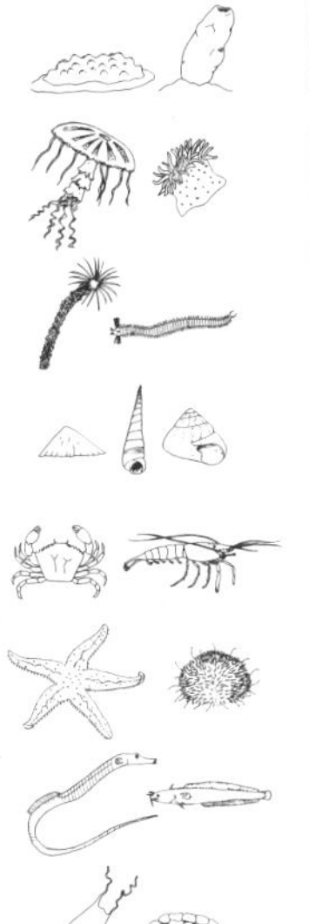

What is it?

If you find an animal or plant on the seashore that you cannot name, and you don't know to which group it belongs, the key below may help.

If it looks...	...and is...	...look in this group
Plant-like	usually found above high tide mark	Lichens p. 60
	brown, green or red - found on all shores below high tide mark	Seaweeds p. 32
	orange, yellow or white sponge-like and branching	Sea Anemones & Relatives p. 76
	or has a delicate branching stem, made up of tiny triangles - found on seaweeds	Sea Anemones & Relatives p. 76
	or has feathery branch-like arms	Starfish & Sea Urchins p. 152

If it looks...	...and is...	...look in this group
Patch-like	hard, pinkish and found clinging to rocks below high tide mark	Seaweeds p. 32
	black, white or orange - covering rocks above high tide	Lichens p. 60
	spongy and bright in colour, covering rocks on the lower shores	Sponges & Similar Animals p. 68
	or appears as groups of tiny cells matted on seaweeds	Sponges & Similar Animals p. 68
	or appear as flat jelly-like patches on seaweeds and rocks, often with beautiful flower-like patterns	Sponges & Similar Animals p. 68

If it looks...	...and is...	...look in this group
Jelly-like with or without tentacles	attached to rocks, with tentacles on top - similar to a blob of jelly when tentacles are hidden	Sea Anemones & Relatives p. 76
	swimming, with tentacles underneath - sometimes washed up on beaches	Sea Anemones & Relatives p. 76
	or appear as flat jelly-like patches on rocks and seaweeds, with beautiful flower-like patterns	Sponges & Similar Animals p. 68
	upright and cylinder-shaped with two openings; often see-through	Sponges & Similar Animals p. 68
Star-like	five-armed, shaped like a star	Starfish & Sea Urchins p. 152

If it looks...	...and appear(s) as...	...look in this group	
Shell-like with no obvious legs	tiny shells firmly attached to rocks 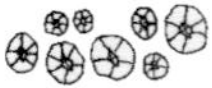	Crabs & Relatives	p. 132
	a round shell, with spines 	Starfish & Sea Urchins	p. 152
	a woodlouse, with overlapping plates on shell	Shells & Relatives	p. 106
	a single shell, with opening for animal 	Shells & Relatives	p. 106
	two shells attached together by a hinge, with animal inside 	Shells & Relatives	p. 106
	a hard tube-like shell firmly attached to rocks 	Worms	p. 92

If it looks...	...and has...	...look in this group
Shell-like with obvious legs	more than five pairs of swimming legs	Crabs & Relatives p. 132
	five pairs of swimming legs and front claws	Crabs & Relatives p. 132
Tube-like	a hard shell-like casing on rocks or tubes in sand or mud	Worms p. 92
Worm-like	**or is** a worm-like animal	Worms p. 92
Fish-like	**or is** actively swimming	Fish p. 168

The Seashore

Twice each day around our coasts, the sea level rises and falls. This is called the tide and it has a huge effect on one of the most fascinating of all environments - the seashore.

Tides

Tides are caused by the effect of the sun's and moon's gravity on the Earth's oceans. This gravity pulls on the oceans, causing water to move away from some areas and gather to form "bulges" in others (see opposite page). In areas where the water "bulges" **high tides** are created, leaving **low tides** where the water has been drawn away.

Every two weeks, when the sun and moon are "in a straight line" with the earth, the pull of gravity is especially strong. This causes very high tides and equally very low tides, which are called **spring tides**.

It is very important to be aware that, during a spring tide, water levels rise very quickly!

When the moon and sun are at right angles to the earth, the effect is not so great, giving less extreme high and low tides. These smaller tides are called **neap tides**.

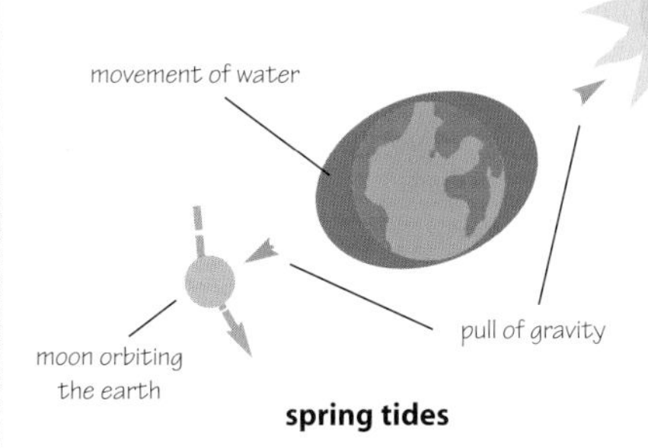

spring tides

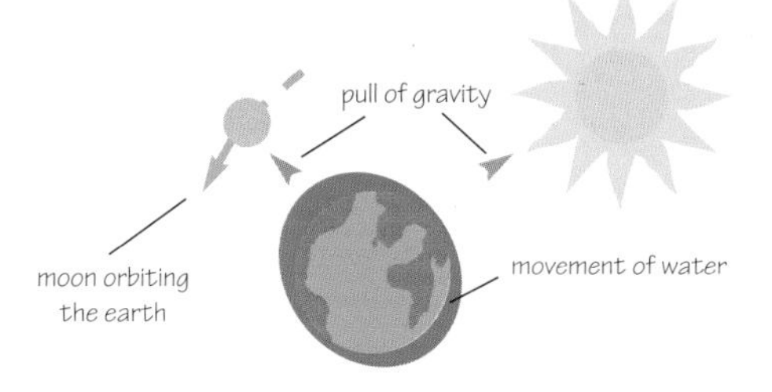

neap tides

Information on tides in your area can be obtained from local newspapers or in special tide-table books (available from boat supply shops and from some newsagents).

Types of seashore

There are many different types of seashore, influenced by a variety of things. Location, rock-formation, exposure to wind and wave action - all have an effect, not only on the appearance of the shore, but on the animals and plants that live there. It is important to learn about these environments and why certain animals and plants survive there.

Rocky shore

Rocky Shores

Rocky shores, whether bedrock (solid rock) or large boulders, provide a wide variety of living spaces, or **habitats**, for animals and plants. Hiding under and attaching themselves to rocks and sheltering in crevices, these animals and plants have a tough life. They have to put up with pounding waves, as well being covered by water and then exposed as the tide rises and falls.

The types of animals and plants found on a rocky shore vary greatly. A lot depends on the type of rock and how sheltered from or exposed to wave action the shore is. On **sheltered shores** the rock surface may be totally covered by seaweeds, due to reduced wave action. These seaweeds provide additional shelter, protection and food for a variety of animals.

On **exposed shores** the constant pounding of waves prevents the growth of much seaweed on the rocks.

A sheltered shore where many seaweeds and animals can settle.

A very exposed shore on which only hardy species can exist.

Animals and plants that live there have to be able to attach themselves firmly to the rocks. Some of the seaweeds that survive there have well-developed **holdfasts** for anchoring themselves, while the animals either cement themselves to the rocks, or hold on using strong sucker feet or sticky discs.

Rockpools

Rockpools are formed when water is caught in the rocks after the tide has gone out. Although the animals and plants that live in rockpools do not have to worry about drying out, they do have to deal with warmer and saltier water. As the sun's rays heat the rockpool, the already salty water evaporates, increasing the salt levels. Then, as the tide comes in again, the rockpools are filled with more seawater and conditions change instantly.

Rockpool

Rockpools are good places in which to look for life, as animals are often trapped in them by the outgoing tide. Watch the pool carefully for signs of movement, taking care not to frighten the animals by letting your shadow fall across the water surface.

Sandy & Muddy Shores

Sandy and muddy beaches may look lifeless, but there are many animals living below the surface. At low tide, the skillful seashore investigator will spot clues which may indicate the presence of an animal - a hole, a burrow, a mound, tracks and trails, or a swirl of sand as something buries itself.

Sandy Shore

Sandy beaches are formed by the action of the waves, which washes small pieces of material from rocks or soil at the land's edge and grinds them down.

Muddy Shore

Muddy shores are usually formed around river **estuaries**, where large mudflats can occur. Soil from fields turns to mud after heavy rain and is washed into the river. As the river reaches the sea it slows down, allowing fine silt particles to settle on the seabed. This silt is then shaped by the tide into soft banks.

There is not a huge variety of animals living on these shores. However, those that have adapted to life in these conditions may be present in large numbers. This is particularly true of muddy beaches, where worms and **molluscs** feed on mud that is full of nutrients.

The shifting sand and mud provide no attachment for seaweeds and the only plant that may be found in these conditions is sea grass (page 59), which is a type of flowering plant.

Muddy shores can be quite dangerous so extra care is needed if you are looking for signs of life.

Shingle beaches

Shingle beaches are the most unfriendly of shores and have little life. Seaweeds cannot attach themselves to the rolling pebbles there, and animals that try to settle can be crushed. Usually, only lichens (page 60) are found on these shores.

Shingle Shore

How the Shore is Divided

All shores are affected by the rise and fall of the tide. As the tide moves up and down each day, different areas are covered by water for different lengths of time.

Each shore can be divided into three main areas, called zones - the **splash zone**, the **intertidal zone** and the **subtidal zone**. The splash zone is the area above the high tide mark. It is rarely, if ever, covered with water, being wet only by salty sea spray or by an extremely high tide. Lichens and land plants are all that survive there, as marine animals and plants need a more definite water-supply. The subtidal zone is the area below low tide; it is continously covered by water, except during extremely low tides. The animals and plants that cannot survive out of water for any period of time, except for very short spells, make their homes there.

The intertidal zone, which is the area of most interest to the seashorer, is between the low tide mark and the high tide mark and this can be divided into the **upper**, **middle** and **lower shore**.

The upper shore spends quite a lot of time out of the water. It is covered by the tide for such a short period each day that conditions are, for much of the time, like those on dry land.

The middle shore is covered by water for longer than the upper shore and so conditions are not as dry.

The lower shore spends most of the day covered by water, rarely drying out or exposing the animals and plants.

The conditions in these areas influence the types of animals and plants found there. Each has learned to adapt to living in a particular area.

On some shores, animals and plants form a visible pattern of bands at different levels. For example, at the top of a rocky shore, on the splash zone, there may be a band of coloured lichens (page 60). Lower down, there may be bands of different brown seaweeds or a band of barnacles (page 150). Each band provides the best conditions for the survival of a particular plant or animal; such survivors are often the main species to be found there. This pattern of bands is called **zonation.**

Banding, or zonation, is not always very obvious. On steeper rocky shores the bands are quite narrow, while on more gently-sloping ones, the bands are much wider. While zonation also applies to sandy, muddy and shingle shores, it is not easy to see, as most animals live underneath the surface.

Zonation

This photograph of a rocky shore is a typical example of zonation, where patterns of banding have been created by various animals and plants. It shows how the shore is divided into different zones and how the animals and plants favour particular areas.

	Some of the main plants & animals likely to be found in the different zones
MHWS **Mean* high-water** level during a **spring tide**	lichens,
MHWN **Mean high-water** level during a **neap tide**	lichens, Channelled Wrack, Spiral Wrack, barnacles
	limpets, barnacles, Bladder Wrack,
MLWN **Mean low-water** level during a **neap tide**	red seaweeds, mussels, barnacles, Serrated Wrack,
MLWS **Mean low-water** level during a **spring tide**	kelps,

*mean = average

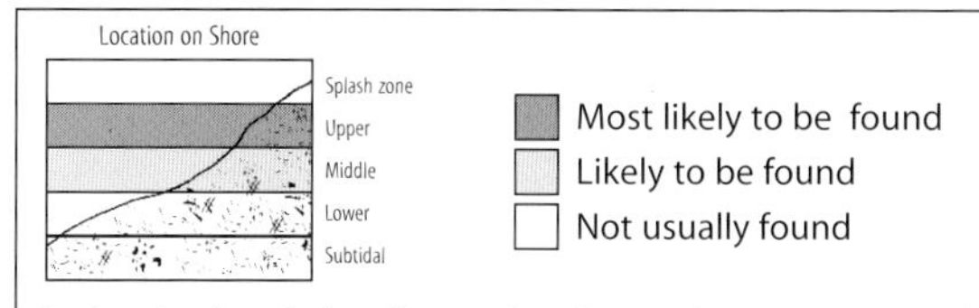

Each animal and plant featured in this guide is accompanied by a shore outline, similar to the one above, showing the particular zones in which they are most likely to be found.

Splash Zone

Wet only by salty sea spray or by an extremely high tide

Intertidal Zone

Between the high tide and low tide mark.

Subtidal Zone

Uncovered by water only during an extremely low tide

Looking for life on the Seashore

Life on the seashore is not easy for the animals and plants living there. They have to survive being covered by water and exposed to air. This is difficult when lungs don't work under water and **gills** cannot work on land.

Animals and plants that live on the shore cannot always be seen. Many of them need to hide from **predators**, which may eat them and some simply need shelter from the drying effects of the sun and wind. A careful search in the right places will help you find some of them:

- under rocks and seaweed where it stays cool and damp, even when the tide is out.
- in crevices, where water may collect.
- on the rock surface. What looks like part of the rock may in fact be a chiton (page 130) or a lichen (page 60).
- on other seaweeds.
- in rockpools.
- buried in the sand or mud. Scoop up some with a spade and put it in a bucket with some water.

Before you set off

Remember, the seashore can be dangerous. Powerful waves may knock you over, strong currents may sweep you out to sea and the incoming tide may trap you on a sand bank or at the base of a cliff. The following guidelines will help you explore safely:

- find out the times of **low** and **high tides** - tide-tables in some local newspapers will give you these. (Tide table books are available from boat supply shops and some newsagents).
- tell someone where you are going.
- don't go alone.
- wear sensible clothing and footwear.

Safety on the Shore

- heed any warning signs.
- start an hour before low tide, so that you are working while the tide is still going out. Keep an eye on the turn of the tide. Remember, the tide rises quickly during a **spring tide** and it can

come in very quickly over a flat, sandy shore.

- work your way up the beach, towards land.
- take extra care if walking on a muddy shore.
- keep away from the water's edge if you can't swim.
- avoid running or jumping; rocks covered in seaweed are slippery.
- look out for waves.
- be careful of what you handle.

Care of the Seashore

The seashore is a very fragile environment. Pollution, litter, trampling on the plants and frightening the animals all cause damage. Take note of the following and you will ensure that the shore is left as you found it.

- don't take animals home, they will not survive for long.
- if you have turned over a rock to see what is underneath, remember to turn it back again. Most animals will not survive if they are left exposed.
- take your litter with you; leave nothing behind.

Some useful equipment

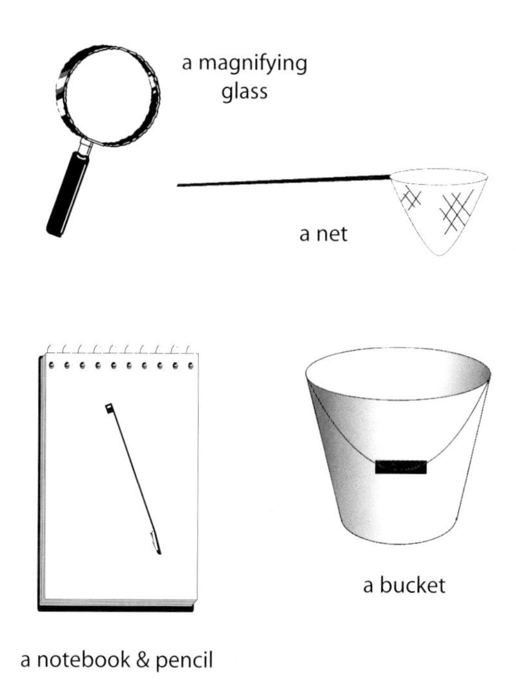

Seaweeds

Everyone is familiar with the plants that grow on land, but plants also grow in the sea. These plants are called **seaweeds** and belong to a group known as **Algae**. Algae are simple plant-like **organisms** that live in water. They can differ in shape and size from single cells to huge plants of up to 60m long. Some algae grow in fresh water, such as rivers and lakes, and others grow in sea water. It is these **marine** algae that make up the huge variety of seaweeds found on the shores and in the shallow waters around our coast. Though some can grow to great lengths, most are quite small.

Seaweeds can grow, make food and reproduce only when covered by water. When uncovered, they are simply surviving until the next high tide. Some seaweeds are able to survive long periods out of water, while others die unless covered by the tide each day. The degree to which they can withstand drying out determines where they can live on the shore. It is sometimes possible to see bands or zones of different seaweeds growing at different levels on the shore (see **Zonation**, page 26). The seaweeds growing there have adapted to life at a particular level. Some, like those growing on exposed shores, have a strong hold on the rocks to prevent them from being torn off by the strong waves. Others, like those growing on the upper shore, have learned to tolerate not only long periods out of water, but also the small amounts of freshwater that run off the land and collect in pools.

Seaweeds play an important role on the shore, providing food and shelter for many animals. They are more plentiful on rocky shores than on sandy beaches, as rocks can provide them with a solid place on which to anchor.

A typical seaweed

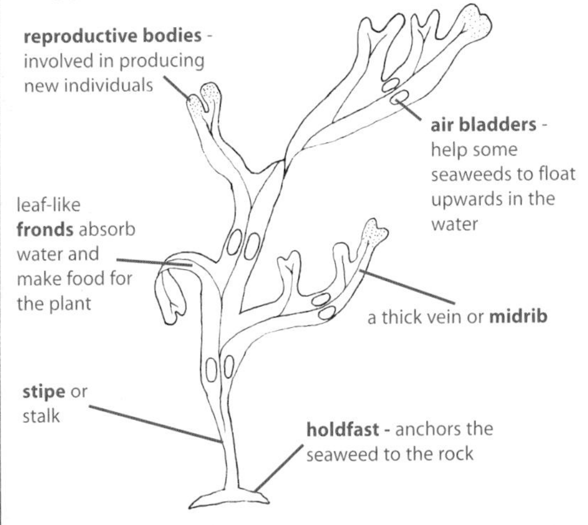

Like land plants, seaweeds need light to grow. They use energy from the sun to produce food. This process is called **photosynthesis**. However, seaweeds differ from land plants in that they do not have leaves, stems or roots. Instead most have **fronds,** which absorb light and water, a **stipe** or stalk, and a **holdfast**, which is used for clinging on to rocks or other surfaces. Often, the holdfast is not very obvious or, in some cases, is not present at all. Many seaweeds may be ripped off the rocks and left to drift in the sea, washing up on the shore on the incoming tide.

Though there are many shapes and sizes of seaweeds, they are divided into three main groups, depending on their colour. These groups are the **greens**, the **browns** and the **reds**. All three groups can be found on the shore, although sometimes the brown seaweeds are so much bigger that they often hide the smaller reds and greens. It is important to be aware that colours can vary with conditions - brown seaweeds can sometimes look olive-green, while some red seaweeds can look brown. When some seaweeds die they lose their colour and become bleached and white.

Because of the possible confusion of colours, the shape of the plant plays an important part in its identification. Of the numerous shapes of seaweeds to be found, a few examples are given opposite.

The first seaweeds you will probably notice on the **middle** and **lower shores** are the wracks and kelps (pages 41-47) . These are among the largest to be found and belong to the brown seaweeds. They often form large blankets of cover, protecting many of the animals and other seaweeds on the shore. They are tougher than most, as they have

Some typical seaweeds

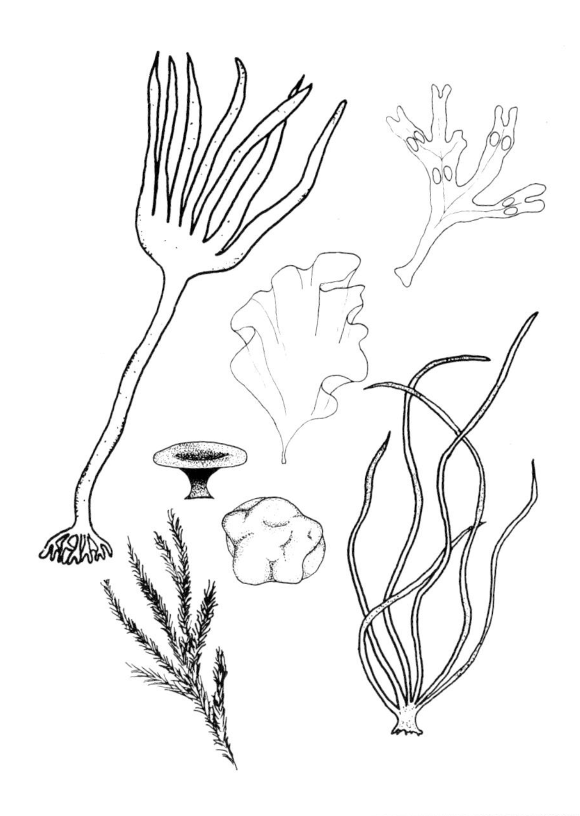

strong leathery fronds and many have a powerful stipe and holdfast. Some wracks also have **air bladders** on their fronds, which enable them to float near the surface where they can absorb more sunlight. **Reproductive bodies** on some seaweeds may look similar to air bladders (see Channelled Wrack, page 41).

Compared to many of the larger brown seaweeds, the greens, reds and other browns are relatively small and often delicate. They can appear lifeless when left uncovered by the sea and may not be easy to identify. In order to see their shape, it is helpful to look at them in water. Many of these seaweeds may not be noticed at first glance and may need to be searched for. Some, however, can be quite obvious, forming striking bands of colour on the shore. An example of this is the green seaweed Link Frond (page 38). Greens, in particular, prefer to grow on the upper shore and in shallow water, where the light is brightest. Red seaweeds like to grow where there is less sunlight, and so they are more often found lower on the shore, frequently shaded by larger seaweeds.

Some seaweeds look nothing like a plant. There are species that form hard crusts on the rocks and which are known as **encrusting seaweeds** (page 58). Others form hard, skeleton-like shapes.

There are many varieties of seaweed, too numerous to mention in this book. We have included only a small selection.

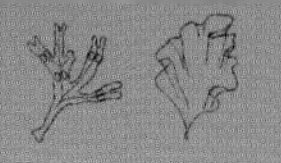

Sea Lettuce

Ulva lactuca

Glasán

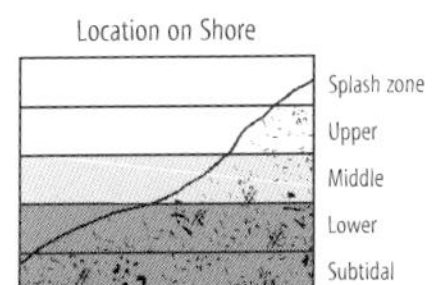

Habitat:	On rocks and in rockpools, often under other seaweeds
Colour:	Bright green
Size:	10-40cm

With a bright green **frond**, the group to which this seaweed belongs is evident. The frond is thin and almost see-through. It is shaped like a lettuce leaf, making it one of the easiest seaweeds to recognise. Sea Lettuce can be found attached to rocks and other seaweeds over the whole shore, as well as in rockpools and in shallow water below the low tide mark. It is common on shores all around Ireland, wherever there is something solid to which it can attach itself.

Link Frond/ Gut Weed

Enteromorpha spp.

Líneáil ghorm

Link Frond is a common seaweed, which is bright green in colour. It has delicate hollow **fronds** that have an inflated and crinkled appearance. Link Frond is found in rockpools and under seaweeds over the whole shore, often forming large blankets of cover. It is one of the few seaweeds that can survive in polluted water and in **brackish water**. When dead, it is often bleached white by the sun.

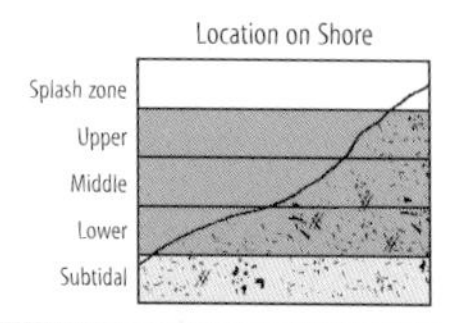

Habitat:	In rockpools, under seaweeds & on open rocks on the shore
Colour:	Bright green, may be bleached by the sun
Size:	10-15cm, but some species are up to 30-40cm

Cladophora rupestris

Cladophora rupestris

Slobán

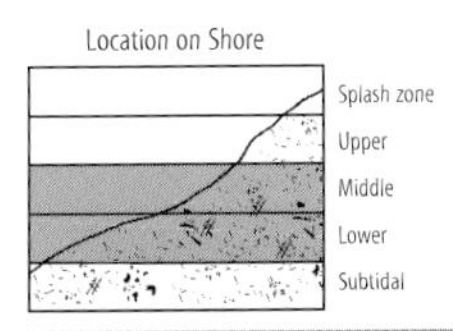

Habitat:	On rocky shores, often under large brown seaweeds
Colour:	Dark green
Size:	7-12cm

Dark green in colour, this seaweed grows in matted clumps of coarse wiry **fronds**. The fronds are heavily branched and often contain trapped mud. *Cladophora rupestris* is usually found underneath the large brown seaweeds growing on the rocks and boulders of the middle and lower shore. This shelter prevents it from drying out.

Velvet Horn

Codium spp.

Beanna Veilbhite

With tubular branching **fronds**, this seaweed looks rather like deer antlers. Dark green in colour, it has a spongy texture and is velvety to the touch, giving rise to its common name, Velvet Horn. This seaweed grows from the middle of the shore down and is usually found on rocks or in rockpools. It has a disc-like **holdfast** made up of a mass of threads tangled together and attached to the rock. Velvet Horn grows more during the winter months, but avoids colder areas.

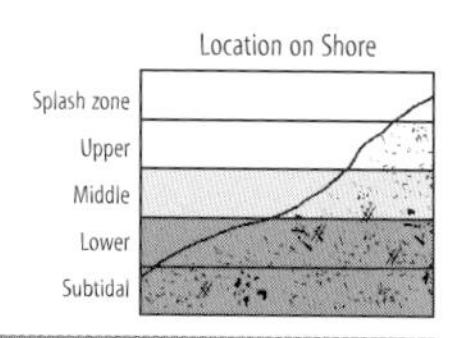

Habitat:	In rockpools & attached to rock on all types of shore
Colour:	Dark green
Size:	25-30cm

Channelled Wrack

Pelvetia canaliculata

Caisíneach

Location on Shore

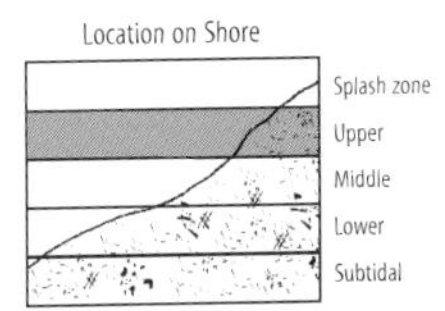

Habitat:	On rocky shores
Colour:	Olive green to orange-brown to dark brown
Size:	5-15cm

This **brown seaweed** gets its name from its **fronds**, which are curled to form a channel on one side. This channel is used to hold water, thus preventing the seaweed from drying out. Because of this, it is able to survive without water for several days on the upper shore. Channelled Wrack is light brown in colour when wet but becomes very dark as it dries out. It has no **midrib** or **air bladders** but has tips that may swell to form **reproductive bodies**.

Spiral Wrack

Fucus spiralis

Casfheamainn

Spiral Wrack is a common **brown seaweed** which is well suited to living on the shore, having tough, flexible and leathery **fronds** that resist damage by waves and exposure to air. The frond of Spiral Wrack has a **midrib** and is slightly twisted; it spirals even more as it dries out. Although it can resist some drying out, Spiral Wrack is not able to survive out of water as well as Channelled Wrack (page 41), so it usually forms a belt slightly lower on the shore.

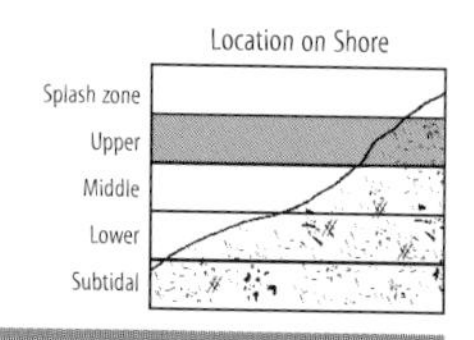

Habitat:	On rocky shores
Colour:	Olive green to orange-brown
Size:	15-20cm

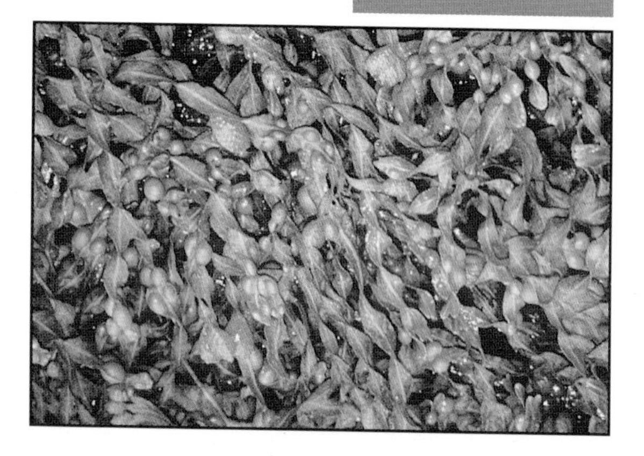

Bladder Wrack

Fucus vesiculosus

Feamainn bhoilgíneach

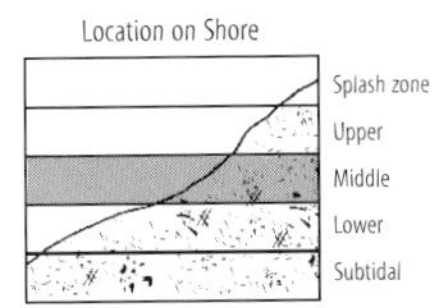

Habitat:	On rocky shores
Colour:	Olive green to yellow-brown
Size:	15-100cm

Bladder Wrack is a type of **brown seaweed**, but, like other wracks, it can sometimes appear olive green. It gets its name from the **air bladders** which are generally found in pairs along the **frond**. There are separate male and female plants, and at certain times of the year orange **reproductive bodies** grow from the ends of the fronds. Bladder Wrack can resist drying out for a short period, but needs to be covered by the tide at least once a day. Because of this, it is usually found attached to rocks and boulders on the middle shore.

Serrated/ Toothed Wrack

Fucus serratus

Míoránach

The saw-like or serrated edge of its **frond** gives this seaweed its common name. The leathery, branching frond is usually olive green in colour, though it may appear orange brown. Unable to survive out of water for long, it is found on the lower shore where its tough, flexible frond helps to reduce damage from wave action and its strong **holdfast** prevents it being washed away. The fronds of Serrated Wrack are often covered by the tiny white spiral tubes of the Coiled Tube Worm (page 96).

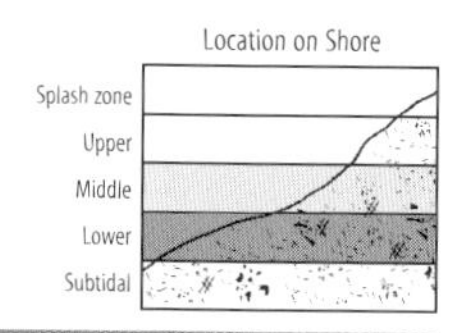

Habitat:	On rocky shores
Colour:	Olive green to brown
Size:	Up to 60cm

Egg/ Knotted Wrack

Ascophyllum nodosum

Feamainn bhuí

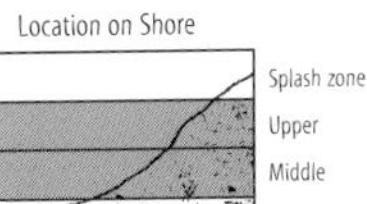

Habitat:	On rocky shores
Colour:	Olive green
Size:	30-150cm

This **brown seaweed** is usually found on fairly sheltered shores, as it has only a small disc-like **holdfast** to grip the rock. The long **fronds** are slightly flattened and have many branches. There is no **midrib** but single egg-shaped **air bladders** that grow along the frond. Each branch usually forms one air bladder a year. By counting them you can get an idea of the age of the seaweed. Egg Wrack often has tufts of a small red seaweed, called *Polysiphonia lanosa* (see inset), growing on it.

Oarweed/ Tangle Kelp

Laminaria digitata

Coirleach

Oarweed belongs to a group of large **brown seaweeds** called kelps. Found on the extreme lower part of the shore, it remains covered by water except at the very lowest spring tides. The long **stipe** of the Oarweed is smooth and flexible. From this grows the **frond**, which is leathery and shiny and divided into strap-like blades. The **holdfast** is large and root-like, firmly attaching the seaweed to the rocks. The holdfast and stipe of this seaweed often provide shelter for a variety of animals and plants.

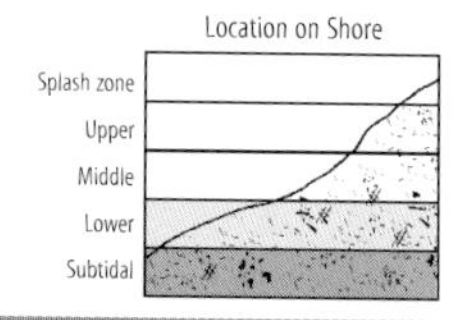

Habitat:	On rocky shores
Colour:	Orange-brown
Size:	1m or more

Sugar Kelp/ Sea Belt

Laminaria saccharina

Rufa

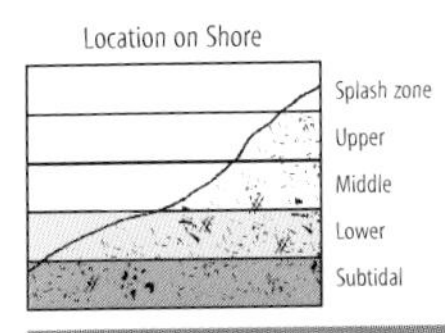

Habitat:	On rocks & stones
Colour:	Orange brown to olive green
Size:	20-300cm

Like the other kelps, Sugar Kelp is found low down on the shore and so is only uncovered by the lowest spring tides. Its long, unbranched, crinkly **fronds** with wavy edges are characteristic, as is the white sugary powder which sometimes coats the frond as it dries. The root-like **holdfast** is smaller than that of Oarweed (page 46) and it has a shorter, slender **stipe**. Perhaps as a result of this, it cannot withstand much wave action and is usually found in more sheltered areas.

Thong Weed

Himanthalia elongata

Ríseach

When young, the individual plants of Thong Weed are shaped like small olive-green buttons (see inset). From each button a long strap-like **frond** grows, which then divides into equally-forked branches. Brown or olive-green in colour, the fronds can grow to over a metre in length and may become a tangled mass. They are tough and leathery, and so resist wave damage on wave-exposed shores.

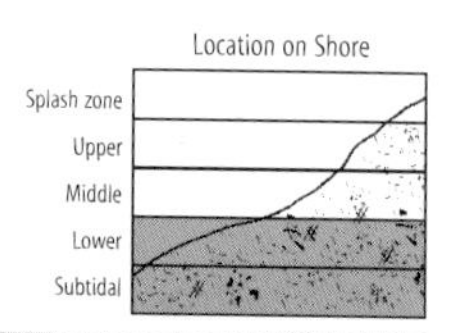

Habitat:	On rocky shores, sometimes in pools
Colour:	Olive-green to brown
Size:	Up to 2m

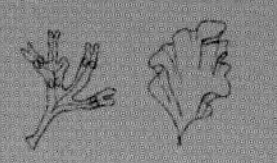

Bootlace Weed

Chorda filum

Ruálach

· Location on Shore

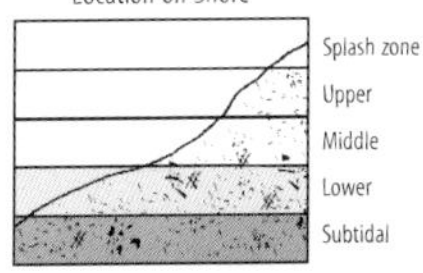

Habitat:	Attached to stones, rocks & shells, often on gravelly shores
Colour:	Olive-brown
Size:	Up to 6m

The long, flowing, cord-like **fronds** of Bootlace Weed are usually found growing together in clumps, giving rise to its alternative name of Mermaid's Tresses. The fronds are dark to olive-brown in colour and when seen under water may appear furry. This is because they are covered in short, fine hairs. It is common on both rocky and gravelly shores, where there are pebbles to which it can attach itself.

Leathesia difformis

Bolgach

Leathesia difformis is an unusual-looking, **brown seaweed** that grows in the shape of knobbly rounded bubbles, around 2-5cm in diameter, and has thick shiny walls. Found on the middle and lower shores, it grows on rocks and other seaweeds. Although solid when young, *Leathesia difformis* becomes hollow as it gets older. It may often be confused with a similar seaweed known as the Oyster Thief, *Colopemnia peregrina*, which differs in that it is covered all over in fine brownish-white dots.

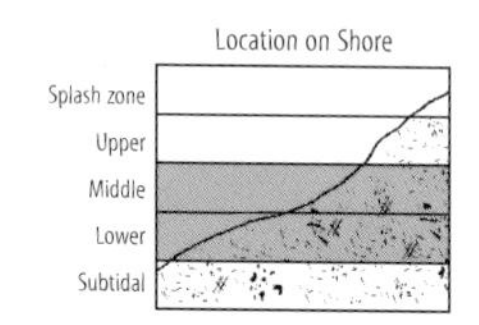

Habitat:	On rocks & smaller seaweeds
Colour:	Olive brown
Size:	2-5cm in diameter

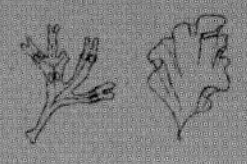

Maiden's Hair

Ectocarpus siliculosus

Folt bé

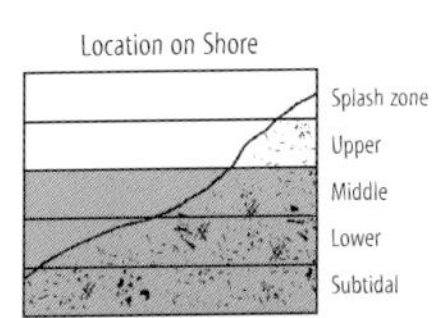

Habitat:	On larger seaweeds, rocks & stones
Colour:	Olive to yellow-brown
Size:	10-30cm

This **brown seaweed** grows in small clumps and can often be found on rocks, loose stones and other seaweeds, from the middle shore down into shallow water. Like many small and delicate seaweeds, it is often overlooked on the shore. When seen in water it has a delicate, feathery appearance, with thin, thread-like, branching **fronds** that are tangled together, becoming free towards the tips. The **holdfast** is fine and creeping, and is very hard to see.

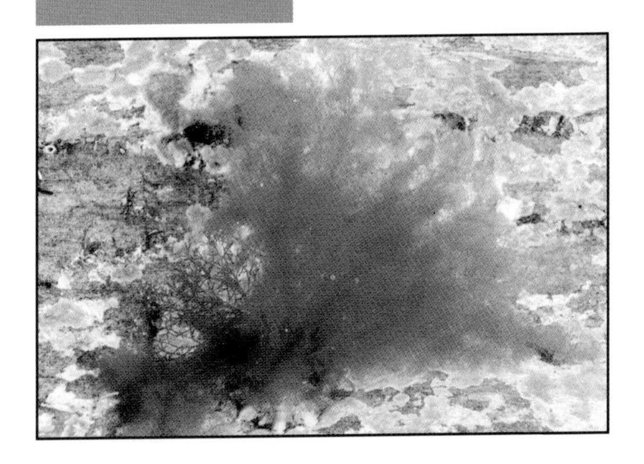

Dulse

Palmaria palmata

Duileasc

Like most **red seaweeds**, Dulse cannot survive drying out but can cope with low light levels. As a result, it is commonly found on the extreme lower shore growing on rocks and on or among the kelps (page 46-47). The tough, flat **fronds** may be bright or dark red and grow from a small, disc-like **holdfast**. The fronds are sometimes divided to form lobes, and small "leaflets" may grow on the sides of older or damaged parts of the plant. It is one of the many red seaweeds that can be dried and eaten.

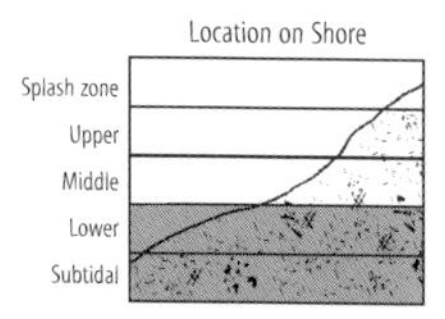

Habitat:	Growing on rocks & other seaweeds
Colour:	Bright to dark red
Size:	20-30cm

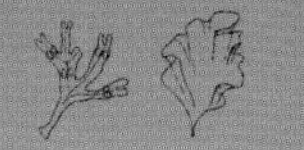

Carrageen/ Irish Moss

Chondrus crispus

Cosáinín (carraige)

Location on Shore

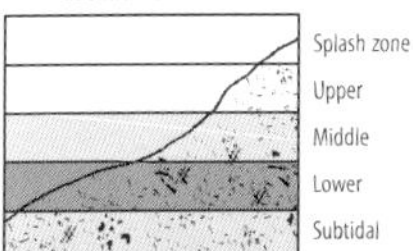

Habitat:	On rocks, under seaweeds & in rockpools
Colour:	Purplish-red
Size:	7-15cm

This is a small, bushy, **red seaweed** with flat **fronds** that regularly divide to form a fan shape. Under water, the tips of the fronds may have a purple/blue shine known as **iridescence** (see below). It is usually found growing underneath the larger brown seaweeds in rockpools, or on rock on the lower shore. It can be dried and used as a food, or as a thickening agent in cooking. The similar *Mastocarpus stellatus* (see inset), has slightly rolled edges to its fronds and a warty surface on older parts. It is also collected as Irish Moss.

Purple Laver

Porphyra spp.

Sleabhac dearg

The almost see-through **fronds** of Purple Laver look like a delicate red version of Sea Lettuce. (page 37) It is commonly found on rocks, among small clumps of mussels (page 122) on exposed wave washed shores, where it can survive drying-out. Its colour varies from rose pink or purple, when seen under water, to almost brown when dry. Some types of Purple Laver are used in Wales to make laverbread. This is made by drying out the seaweed, mixing it with oatmeal and frying it.

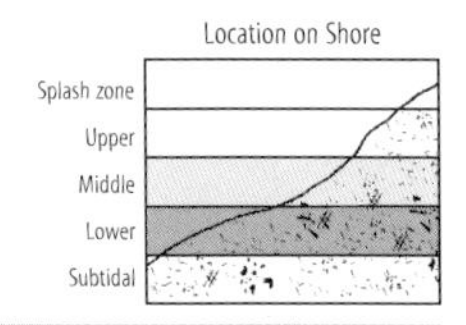

Habitat:	On stones and rocks, especially in exposed areas
Colour:	Rose-red, purple or brown when dry
Size:	Up to 20cm

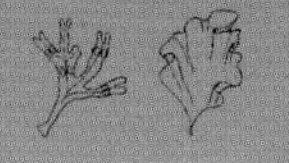

Lomentaria articulata

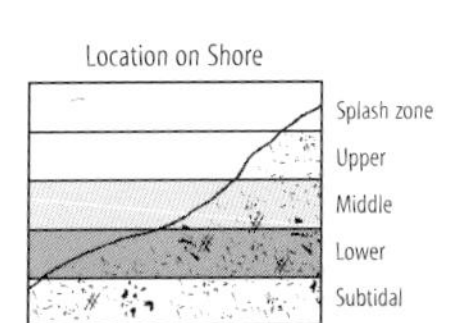

Habitat:	Attached to rock & other seaweeds
Colour:	Bright red
Size:	5-25cm

This seaweed is bright red in colour and has shiny **fronds** which may appear **irridescent** when covered with water. The branched fronds are hollow and form a chain that looks like a string of oval-shaped beads. It can grow up to 25cm in length and form a dense mass, although it is more often found in smaller clumps. It usually grows on other seaweeds, attached to rocks on the middle and lower shores.

Pepper Dulse

Laurencia pinnatifida

Míobhán

Pepper Dulse is found growing close to the rock in large patches, often in crevices, from the middle shore down to shallow water. It has flattened **fronds** and a tufted appearance. Its colour can vary, depending on where it is on the shore. It is usually a purple-brownish colour, often with bleached tips, but can appear green-yellow on the middle shore. Its common name comes from its strong peppery taste.

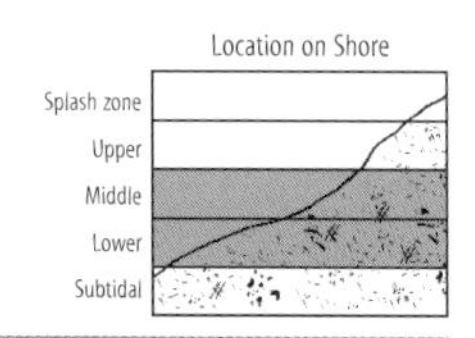

Habitat:	On rocky shores, often in crevices
Colour:	Purple to yellowish-brown or greenish-yellow
Size:	Up to 20cm but usually smaller

Coral Weed

Corallina officinalis

Feamainn choiréalach

Location on Shore

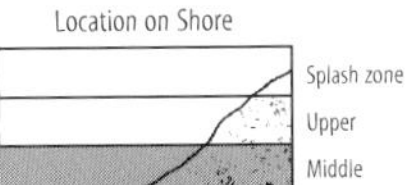
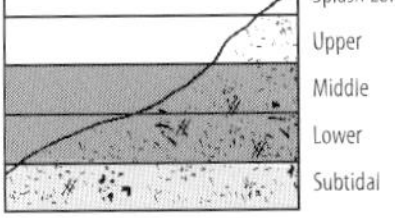

Habitat:	On rocks & in rockpools & crevices
Colour:	Pink to purple
Size:	Up to 12cm

Although this is a type of red seaweed, it is actually pink in colour and has a stone-like texture. Coral Weed has a segmented, chalky, skeleton-like structure which gives the seaweed its jointed appearance. This type of seaweed can grow in crevices and rockpools on the rocky shore. The **calcareous** "skeleton" often remains when the plant has washed up, where it may become bleached by the sun.

Pink Encrusting Seaweeds

Lithophyllum spp. & *Lithothamnion* spp.

Gruánach

These **red seaweeds** do not look like "normal" seaweeds seen on the shore. They give the impression that the rock on which they live has been painted a pinkish colour. They form patchy crusts, which may be smooth or lumpy, and so are called "encrusting" seaweeds. They are found in pools and on rocks and stones on the lower part of the shore. They can cover large areas, completely lining damp crevices and small pools. When dead, these seaweeds can turn a yellowish-white.

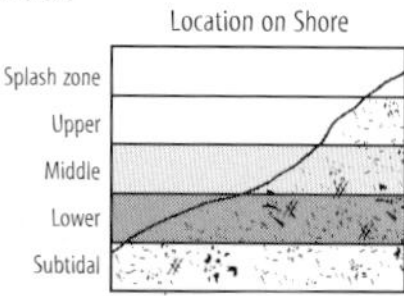

Habitat:	In rockpools, on stones & rocks, often in exposed areas
Colour:	Ranging from pale pink to purple or yellowish-white when dead
Size:	Can cover large or small areas

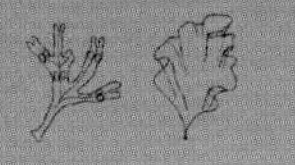

Eelgrass/ Sea Grass

Zostera marina

Miléarach

Location on Shore

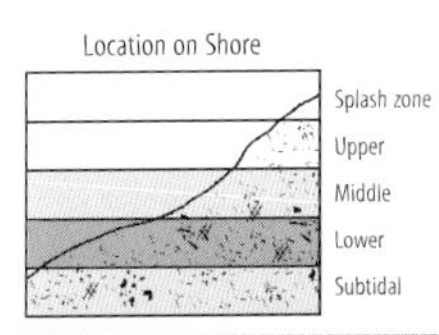

Habitat:	On gravel, sand or mud, often in sheltered estuaries
Colour:	Dark or grass green
Size:	Up to 1m

Eelgrass is not an **Alga** but a dark green, flowering plant. It can be found growing in mud, sand or fine gravel, mainly in the sheltered water of **estuaries**. It is totally **marine**, occurring from the middle shore down to shallow waters, but closely resembles the grasses found on land. Its leaves are long, narrow and flattened, with rounded tips and a series of veins running up their length. They can grow up to 1m long, though they are usually much smaller.

Lichens

On the seashore, **lichens** are usually found high up on the **splash zone**. They are unusual plants in that they are made up of tiny **algae** and a **fungus** living together as one. The algae live on the inside of the plant, producing food, while the fungus lives on the outside providing shape, shelter and support for the algae. The algae make food by **photosynthesis**. They take in carbon dioxide and water and, with the help of sunlight, make sugar. The fungus, which cannot make food for itself, then feeds on this sugar.

The main body of the lichen is called the **thallus** and in different species the shape and texture can vary. Some are branched, leafy or tufted, while others are flat and encrusting. Some feel brittle and rough, while others are soft or smooth to the touch. Lichens also come in a huge variety of colours and it is important to remember that the colour often changes when they are wet.

Lichens do not have "true" roots, but can absorb water quickly through the thallus from rain, sea spray, fog and dew. If there is no moisture, lichens quickly dry out and stop making food. However, they become active again once water is absorbed. Their growth is relatively slow, from as little as 1mm or less per year, up to a few centimetres per year.

Able to survive in harsh conditions, lichens often form patches on cliffs and rocks. They can live on any surface that does not flake or erode too quickly, provided they have enough light and water. They exist in many different environments, from tropical to arctic, and many live for thousands of years.

Lichens play an important part in the environment, slowly helping to break down rocks to make soil and also helping to measure levels of pollution, as lichens can absorb chemicals from the air.

Some typical lichens

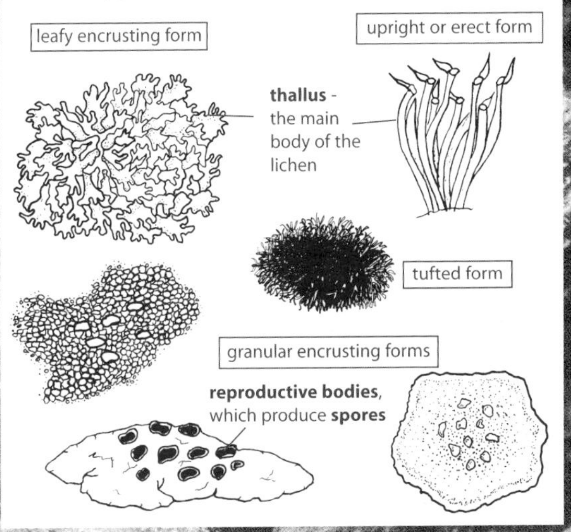

Black Tufted Lichen

Lichina pygmaea

Léicean dosach dubh

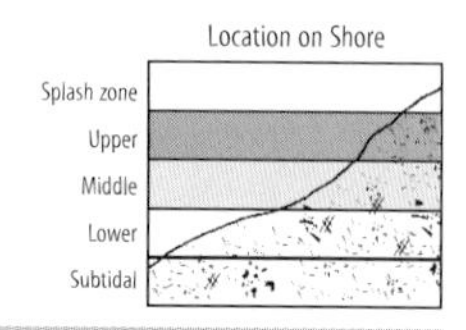

Habitat:	On rocky shores, especially exposed sites
Colour:	Brownish-black to yellowish-brown
Size:	1.5cm high

This lichen, which resembles a small seaweed, is coarsely tufted and grows in small patches of up to 1.5cm high. Dark brown to black in colour, it sometimes has yellow-brown branches. It is common on all rocky coasts, even on the steepest wave-exposed sites. It is often found among barnacles (page 150) on the upper shore, below the the high tide mark. A very similar lichen is *Lichina confinis*, which has shorter tufts and can be found a little higher up on the shore, in the splash zone.

Black Tar Lichen

Verrucaria spp.

Léicean dubh tarra

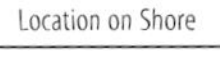

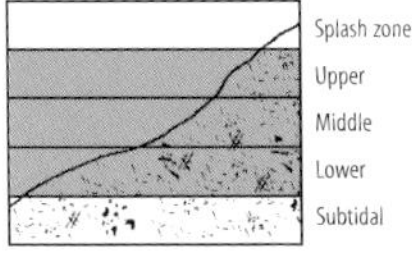

Habitat:	Encrusting on rocks
Colour:	Green-black to black
Size:	Patches may cover large areas

Black Tar Lichen is commonly found on all coasts, whether sheltered or exposed. Several closely-related and similar species can be found. All form a thin, black crust on the rocks which sometimes looks like a patch of oil or paint. The patches vary in size, from less than 30cm to several metres in diameter. Some patches feel slimy to the touch and appear green-black when scraped off the rock, while others feel dry and granular and are black in colour.

Orange Leafy Lichen

Xanthoria spp.

Léicean duilleach flannbhuí

The **thallus** of the Orange Leafy Lichen is rough and leaf-like and can vary in colour from yellow to bright orange. It is very common on both sheltered and exposed shores, and occurs just above the level of the highest tides in the splash zone. It can be seen in irregular patches of up to 10cm in diameter. This lichen is very common in areas that are rich in nutrients. As with some other lichens, this particular species was onced used to make many natural dyes of yellow and crimson.

Location on Shore

Splash zone	
Upper	
Middle	
Lower	
Subtidal	

Habitat:	On rocks on most shores
Colour:	Yellow-orange
Size:	Patches up to 10cm in diameter

Orange Lichen

Caloplaca marina

Léicean flannbhuí

Location on Shore

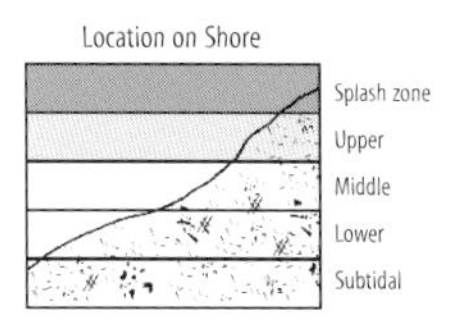

Habitat:	Encrusting on rocks
Colour:	Dark orange
Size:	Patches up to 10cm in diameter

This dark Orange Lichen is often found, along with Black Tar Lichen (page 63), on the upper part of the shore. It is flat and encrusting in appearance, forming irregular granular patches of up to 10cm in diameter. The saucer-shaped, **spore**-producing structures are a darker orange with slightly paler edges. This lichen is found on both sheltered and exposed shores.

Sea Ivory

Ramalina siliquosa

Eabhar mara

The stiff, upright tufts of Sea Ivory have strap-like branches which are greenish-grey in colour and have a smooth, brittle texture. The branches may bear pale brown, disc-like **reproductive bodies** at their tips. The tufts may grow up to 5cm long in sheltered areas. It is usually found on the extreme upper shore, among other lichens and can be very plentiful on rocks.

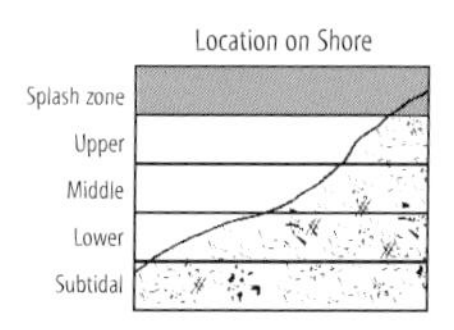

Habitat:	On rocks on both sheltered & exposed shores
Colour:	Pale greenish-grey
Size:	2-5cm long

Black Shields

Lecanora atra

Scála dubh

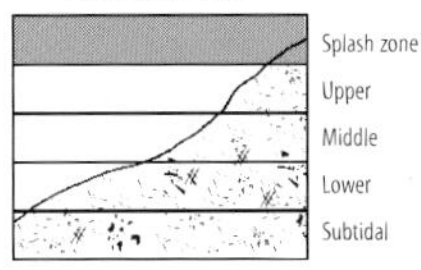

Habitat:	Encrusting on rocks on all shores
Colour:	Whitish-grey, with black markings
Size:	Up to 10cm in diameter

Black Shields is found above the high tide mark, often along with the Orange Leafy Lichen (page 64). It forms whitish-grey, irregular patches, with cracked, rough surfaces. The centre of the patches may sometimes bear black, saucer-shaped **reproductive bodies** which carry the **spores**. A similar white lichen, *Ochrolechia parella*, can be recognised by its pale grey spore structures and more rounded patches (see inset).

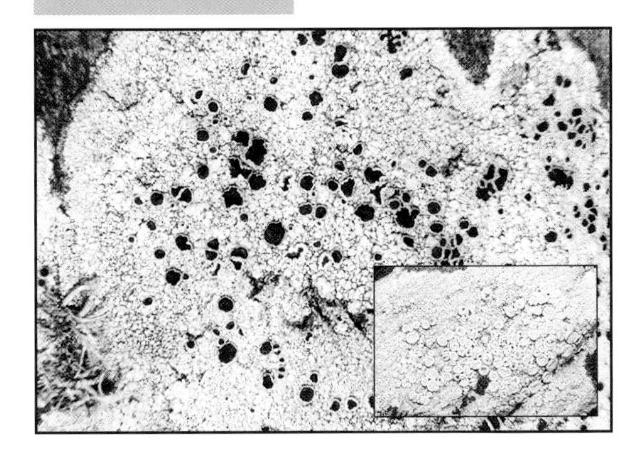

Sponges & Similar Animals

Turn over a rock on the **lower shore** and the underside is often a patchwork of colourful **encrusting animals** that are permanently fixed there - sponges, sea mats and sea squirts. Many of these animals are actually hundreds of tiny individuals living together in a group, or **colony**.

A typical sponge

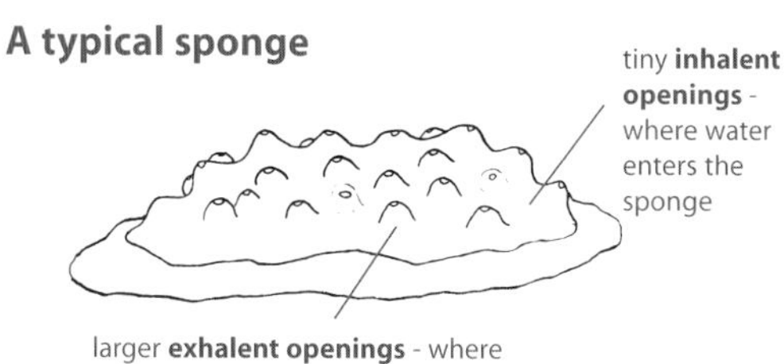

Sponges are very simple animals. They are usually found on the lower shore, underneath rocks and in damp crevices. They feed by taking water into the body and filtering out the tiny particles of food, which they then absorb. The shape of the body varies, but basically consists of an internal skeleton supporting a series of canals which carry water to all parts. These canals are connected to the outside by a number of openings. The food-filled water enters through many tiny surface pores, called **inhalent openings**, and the waste is pumped out through a few larger openings, called **exhalent openings**.

The adult sponges live permanently attached to rocks or shells, but have free swimming larvae (eggs) which enable the young to spread to other areas. In exposed areas where there are strong water currents or breaking waves, sponges tend to grow with rounded or flattened shapes, to avoid damage. In more sheltered areas, they can grow more upright, often with delicate branching shapes.

A typical sea mat

Sea mats usually form thin patches on seaweeds, rocks and seashells. These patches often feel chalky or slimy to the touch and are made up of hundreds of tiny animals called zooids. Under a microscope, it can be seen that each animal lives in its own box-like capsule and has a crown of **tentacles**, which it waves in the water to catch tiny particles of food.

Typical sea squirts

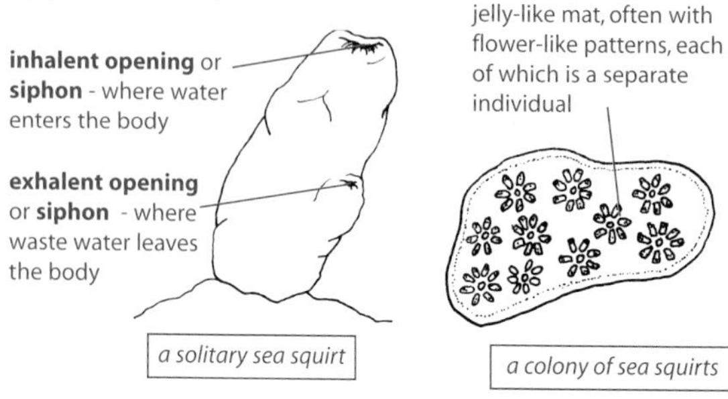

a solitary sea squirt

a colony of sea squirts

Although **sea squirts** may appear similar to sponges, they are actually quite complex animals. Sea squirts have a sac-like body which may be jelly-like or have a leathery feel. They have large **inhalent** and **exhalent openings** called **siphons**, through which water enters and leaves the body. The water brings with it particles of food which the sea squirt filters through a mucus sieve.

Some sea squirts live in colonies, forming jelly-like mats. These mats often have beautiful flower-like patterns. Others live as single individuals. These **solitary** sea squirts can grow quite large, especially in areas where damage from waves is unlikely. If gently squeezed, a jet of water squirts out of the exhalent opening. This has given rise to their common name.

Breadcrumb Sponge

Halichondria panicea

Spúinse grabhrógach

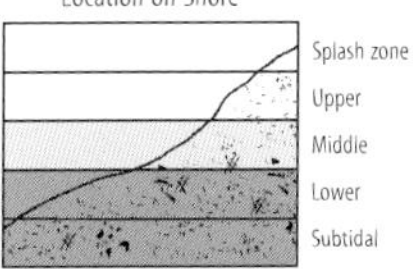

Habitat:	Encrusting on rocks, stones, shells & seaweeds
Colour:	Yellow, pale green & occasionally orange
Size:	Patches of various sizes

One of the commonest sponges to be found on the seashore, the Breadcrumb Sponge, forms encrusting patches on rocks and on the stems of kelp seaweeds (page 46-47). Varying in colour from yellow to pale green, it has a distinctive appearance. The smooth surface is dotted with volcano-shaped openings which are called **exhalent openings**. The **inhalent openings** are too small to see. When handled, the crumbly-textured sponge breaks easily and gives out a strong bread-like smell, hence its common name.

Hymeniacidon perleve

Hymeniacidon perleve

This deep orange-coloured sponge is often found alongside the Breadcrumb Sponge. It can be distinguished from it by its colour, its lumpy surface and the fact that the openings are not usually volcano-shaped. It forms irregular patches in crevices, under overhangs or among kelp (page 46-47). It can also be found partly submerged in mud, attached to a hard structure. There is another sponge called *Myxilla incrustans* which is quite similiar to this, and it can be hard to tell them apart by sight.

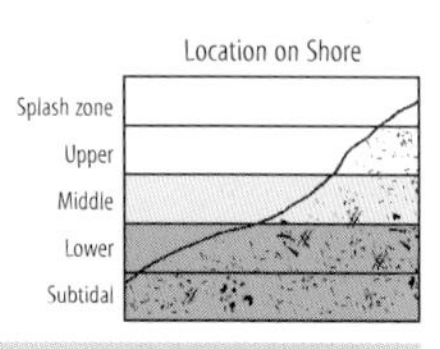

Habitat:	On rocky shores, especially in crevices, under overhangs & on holdfasts
Colour:	Deep orange to red
Size:	Patches of various sizes

Sea Mat

Membranipora membranacea

Milseán mara

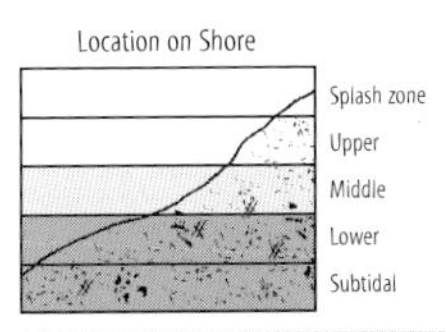

Habitat:	Encrusting on kelps & other seaweeds
Colour:	White
Size:	Patches can cover large areas

The common Sea Mat forms thin white patches on the stems and **fronds** of kelp (page 46-47) and other seaweeds. A closer look with a magnifying glass reveals a delicate lacy pattern of miniature rectangular boxes, each of which contains a tiny animal. Other species of Sea Mat can also be found on the seashore. The Hairy Sea Mat forms off-white or reddish-brown patches and is especially common on the brown seaweed, Serrated Wrack (page 44). As its name suggests, these patches are covered in short bristles.

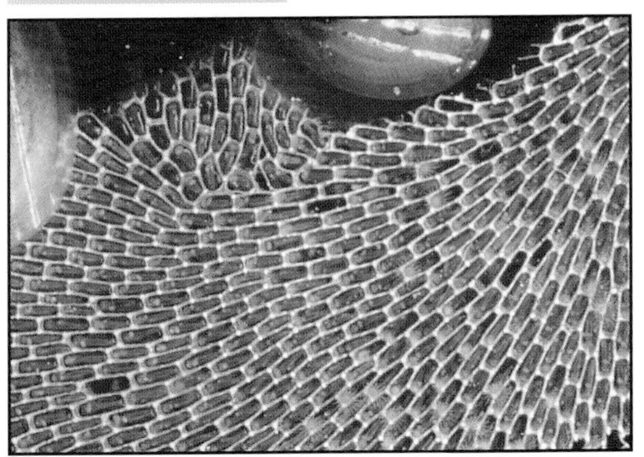

Star Ascidian

Botryllus schlosseri

Ascaid réaltach

The Star Ascidian is one of the most attractive and colourful sea squirts to be found on our shores, forming thick, jelly-like patches on rocks and seaweeds. Found on the lower shore and in shallow waters, this sea squirt lives in a **colony**, with the individual animals forming flower or star-shaped groups around a common **exhalent opening.** On lighter-coloured species, the **inhalent openings** on each individual sometimes appear as a red spot.

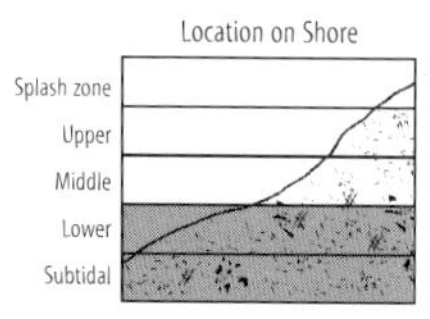

Habitat:	Encrusting on rocks & shells & large brown seaweeds
Colour:	Varies greatly, often brightly coloured with "stars" in a contrasting colour
Size:	Patches vary in size

Sea Squirt

Ascidiella aspersa

Ascaid

Location on Shore

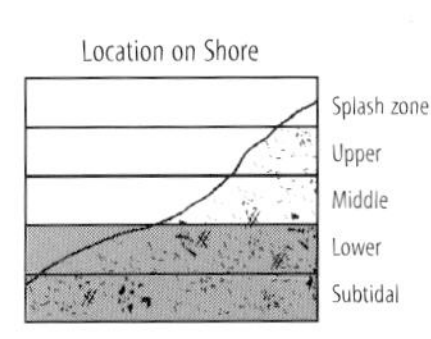

Habitat:	Attached to rocks and seaweeds
Colour:	White
Size:	Up to 13cm

Unlike the Star Ascidian (page 74), this Sea Squirt is a single individual and is found attached to rocks and seaweed on the lower shore, down to deeper waters. Its body is soft, cylinder-shaped and often quite see-through. It has two openings, one called the **inhalent siphon** and the other the **exhalent siphon**. When feeding, it draws in water through the inhalent siphon, filters out the tiny particles and then passes the water out through the exhalent opening.

Sea Anemones & Relatives

Sea anemones and jellyfish belong to a group of animals known as **cnidarians** (pronounced nid-ar-ians) - the jelly animals. These animals often resemble flowers, with their soft, colourful, sac-like body and rings of **tentacles** around the mouth. They can be found as single individuals, which are known as **polyps**, or joined with others to form a group or **colony**.

Cnidarians have many tiny stinging cells on their tentacles, which they use for self-defence and to catch food. In some species, the sting is powerful enough to be dangerous to humans.

To identify the different **sea anemones**, the features we usually use are colour, shape and tentacle number. You should keep in mind, though, that colour, in particular, may vary in different environments. The anemones that live on rocky shores attach themselves firmly to rocks and stones with a sticky **basal disc**, but are still able to move. In anemones that live on soft muddy shores, the basal disc and **column** have adapted to burrowing. Sea anemones often appear like blobs of jelly on the shore, as many are able to pull in their tentacles. They react

A typical sea anemone

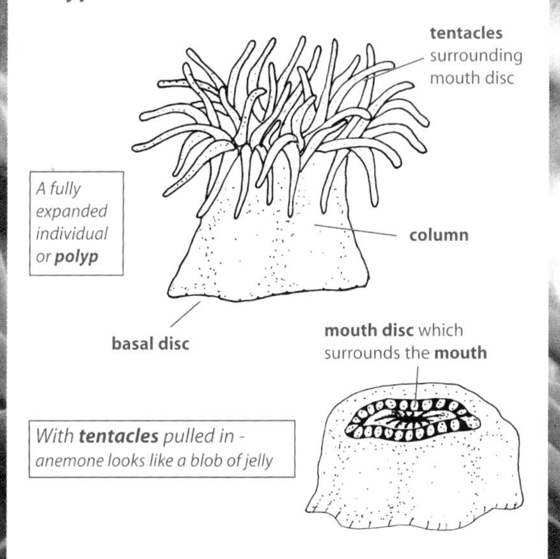

like this if they are disturbed, or when the tide goes out, as it helps prevent drying out and damage.

Anemones are **solitary** or single cnidarians and, although many may cover a rock surface, they are not joined in any way. Their close relatives, the jellyfish, are similar but they inhabit the open sea and are found on the shore only when stranded.

Jellyfish have a soft bell-shaped body with tentacles underneath. These tentacles, which can have quite a dangerous sting, catch food such as **plankton** and small animals in the water and also help the jellyfish protect itself from attackers. Jellyfish can be identified by the colour and pattern of the markings on their body. Although some jellyfish have only a very mild sting, others can be quite dangerous so it is best not to touch any of them - just in case!

A typical jellyfish

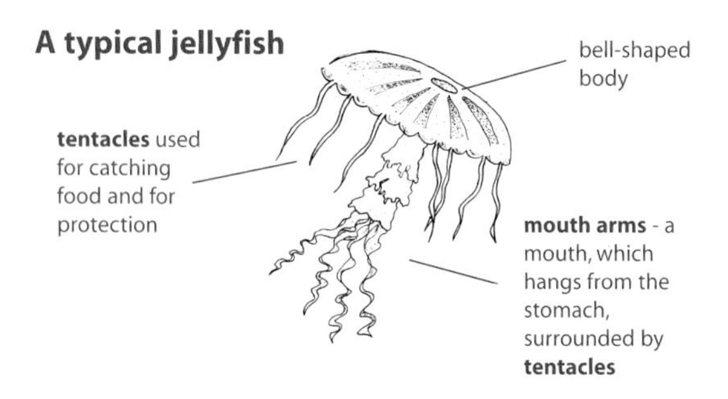

Other members of the cnidarian family include **hydroids**, **soft corals** and **hard corals**. These are formed by many polyps (individuals) living together in a colony.

Looking like tiny ferns or fir trees, hydroids are sometimes known as sea firs (page 88). They are especially common on rocky shores, where they are found attached to rocks, seaweeds and other animals. Their often minute size and delicate, twig-like shapes can make them difficult to see. However, some species can grow much larger.

A typical hydroid

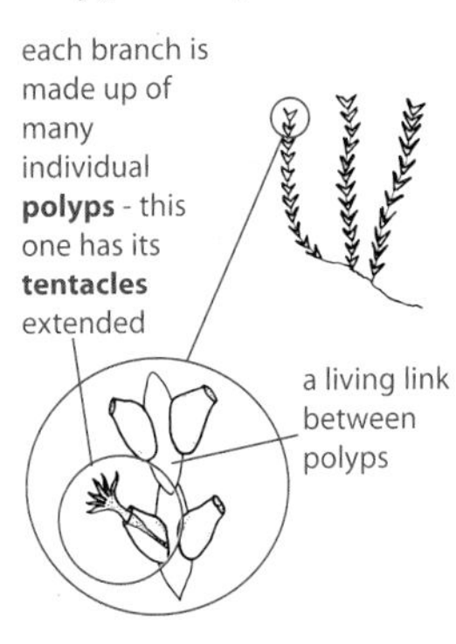

Soft corals and hard corals are colonies of polyps (individuals) that live together in skeleton-like structures. These structures, which usually attach themselves to rocks and stones, protect the delicate polyps. An example of soft coral is the Dead Man's Finger (page 87). When covered by water, the little polyps can be seen feeding. These pull in and hide, however, when disturbed or uncovered by water.

A typical soft coral

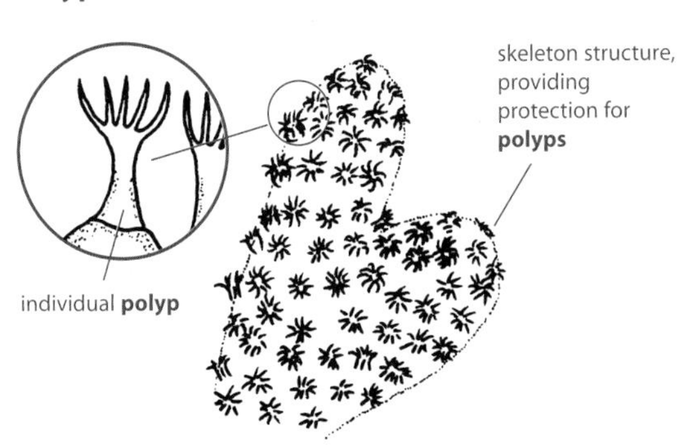

Beadlet Anemone

Actinia equina

Bundún coirníneach

This is the most common anemone found on rocky shores around Ireland, and is often first noticed as a blob of jelly on the rocks. It is usually red in colour but there are also green and orange-brown varieties. Look out for the blue, bead-like warts at the base of the **tentacles**, and a thin blue line edging the base of the **column**. By pulling in its tentacles at low water, the anemone reduces water loss. A slimy mucus coating also helps to keep moisture in.

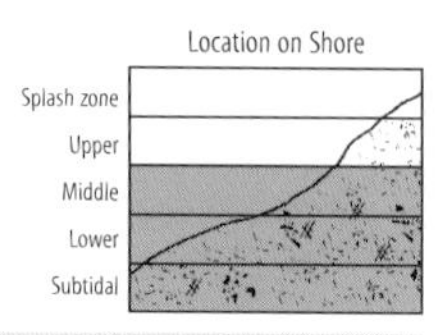

Habitat:	On the rocky shore, in crevices, rockpools & under seaweeds
Colour:	Varies from red to orange to green to brown, with blue warts
Size:	2-7cm in diameter

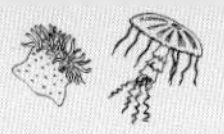

Snakelocks Anemone/Opelet

Anemonia viridis
(Anemonia sulcata)

Bundún nathairiúil

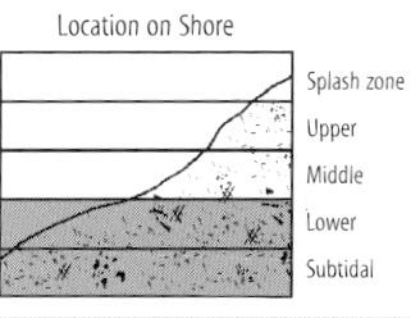

Habitat:	On rocks & in well lit rockpools
Colour:	Varies greatly from green to brown to grey, often with purple tips on tentacles
Size:	Column up to 5cm long

Up to two hundred snake-like waving **tentacles**, which can grow to a length of more than 12cm, give this anemone its name. As it cannot draw these into its body when disturbed, or when the tide goes out, it prefers to remain in water and is often found in rockpools, in damp crevices or on seaweeds. The colour of the Snakelocks Anemone varies from green through grey and brown, sometimes with purple tips on the tentacles. The **column** is smooth and quite long.

Dahlia Anemone

Urticina felina

(Tealia felina)

Bundún leice dáilia

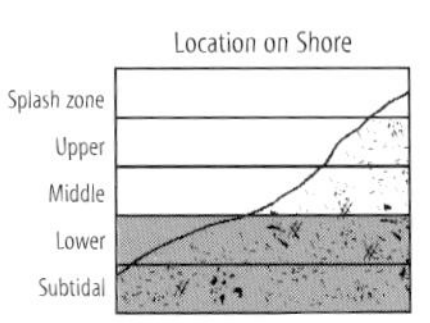

Habitat:	In rockpools & in shady crevices on rocky shores
Colour:	Varies greatly with some beautifully coloured markings
Size:	Up to 15cm in diameter when fully expanded

This is the largest anemone to be found on the shore. It gets its name from its stunning, flower-like appearance. The short, stubby **tentacles** and **mouth disc** are patterned with bands of colour ranging from blues and greens to pinks and reds. A strong, sucker-like base ensures firm attachment to the rock, even in the most wave-swept sites. The **column** is often covered with warts to which bits of shell and gravel stick, providing a good disguise when the tentacles are drawn inside.

Gem/Wartlet Anemone

Aulactinia verrucosa
(Bunodactis verrucosa)

Bundún na seod

Location on Shore

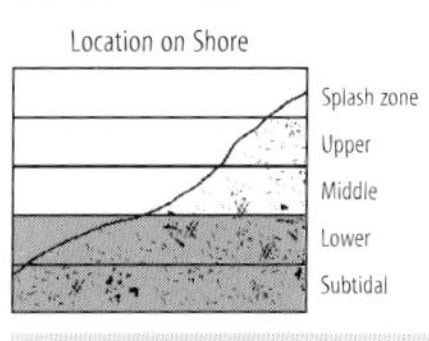

Habitat:	In well-lit rockpools & crevices on rocky shores
Colour:	Pink with grey-green tinge & rows of white warts on column
Size:	Up to 3cm diameter

This small anemone gets one of its common names from its warty appearance when closed. It is often found in well-lit rockpools and crevices, where its pinkish-coloured body provides good camouflage against a background of pink encrusting and coralline seaweeds (pages 57-58). The 48 transparent **tentacles** grow to 1.5cm and may be patterned with greyish-green bands. The fairly short **column** bears 6 rows of white warts, as well as numerous darker ones, which make it easy to identify.

Daisy Anemone

Cereus pedunculatus

Nóinín mara

This anemone has a wide mouth surrounded by many (700+) short **tentacles**. When open, these lie flat on the surface of the mud or sand. The rest of the anemone lies buried in muddy sand, firmly anchored to a stone or shell. The **column** is trumpet-shaped and orange to grey-brown in colour. The **mouth disc** and tentacles are usually darker, and may be patterned with shades of cream and dark brown. This anemone can also be found deep in crevices on the rocky shore.

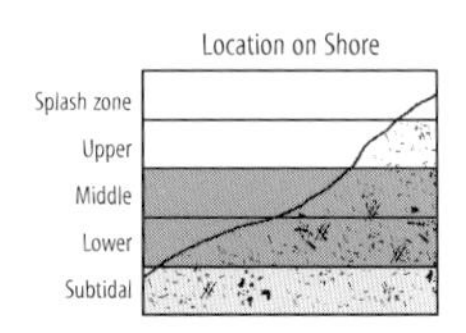

Habitat:	On rocky shores, in crevices & buried in muddy sand
Colour:	Orange to grey-brown column, tentacles darker & may be patterned
Size:	Up to 3cm across

Plumose Anemone

Metridium senile

Bláth mara

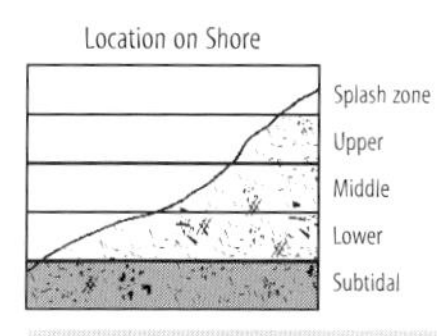

Habitat:	Attached to rocks, piers & wrecks
Colour:	Varies - white, cream, orange, olive, brown
Size:	8cm or more high

This anemone has many **tentacles** which are closely crowded together. When fully expanded underwater, it looks like a powder puff. The tall **column** is smooth and of a single colour. When closed, the anemone shrinks into a flattened blob. There are several colour varieties, including orange, white, brown and cream. Although mainly found in shallow and deeper waters, it can sometimes be found in rockpools, under boulders and on piers at low spring tides.

Burrowing Anemone

Peachia cylindrica

(Peachia hastata)

Bundún uachaise

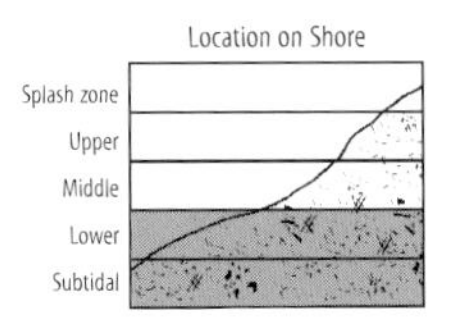

Habitat:	Buried in sandy mud, sand or gravel
Colour:	Pinkish & creamy-beige or brown with darker brown markings
Size:	Commonly 6cm long & 2cm across

This anemone does not need a pebble or shell to attach to, as its worm-like body burrows through muddy sand. The long, thin **column** can extend up to 15cm and is a pinkish-brown, sometimes with paler vertical lines. The column almost always lies buried in the sand, with just 12 **tentacles** and the **mouth disc** showing on the surface. The tentacles are creamy beige and brown in colour, with quite obvious w-shaped cream markings.

Dead Man's Fingers/Soft Coral

Alcyonium digitatum

Méara mara

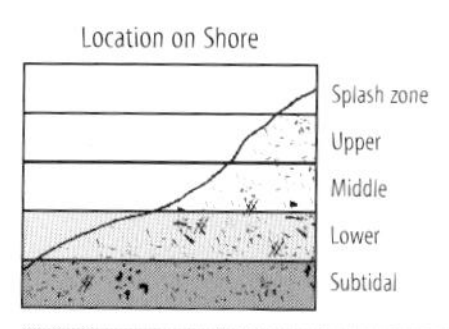

Habitat:	On rocks, stones, wrecks or piers
Colour:	Orange or white colony with white polyps
Size:	Up to 20cm high

Dead Man's Fingers get their gruesome name from their resemblance to soft, bloated fingers. A relative of sea anemones and coral, each "finger" is actually a whole group, or **colony**, of animals living together. These upright branching structures are home to hundreds of tiny, white feeding **polyps**, each of which looks like a single, small sea anemone and which grows to about 1cm. Colonies may grow to a height of up to 20cm and, though common in deeper waters, around piers and wrecks, may only be seen on the shore at really low tide.

Sea Fir

Dynamena pumila

Giúis mhara

Sea Fir is a tiny relative of the sea anemone and is known as a **hydroid**. It lives in a **colony**, or group, that looks very like a tiny upright branching stem. The structure of the stem (which is best seen with a hand lens) looks like a chain, making this a fairly easy hydroid to identify. Sea Fir is quite a common species of hyroid and is often found growing on seaweeds (particularly Serrated Wrack - page 44) and on rocks on the lower shore.

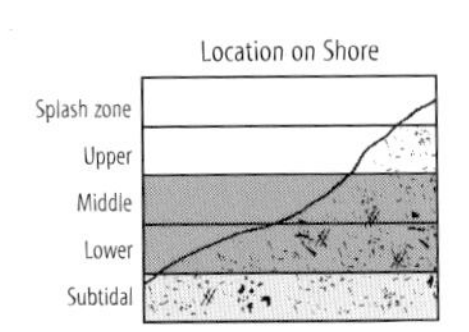

Habitat:	Grows on rocks & seaweeds
Colour:	Whitish-orange
Size:	Up to 3cm

Common Jellyfish

Aurelia aurita

Smugairle róin coiteann

Location on Shore

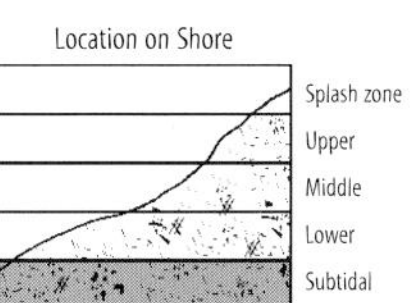

Habitat:	Floats out at sea but may be seen washed up on beaches
Colour:	Almost see-through with purple markings
Size:	Up to 25cm across

The Common Jellyfish is a free-floating animal that feeds on a wide range of **plankton** and small fish. It has a saucer-shaped and jelly-like body that can grow up to 25cm in diameter, with four purplish **mouth arms** hanging below. On the top of its body, it has four purple horseshoe-shaped rings which are its **reproductive organs**. The common jellyfish is most often seen as a transparent blob of jelly washed up on the shore, and may be present in large numbers in coastal waters during the summer.

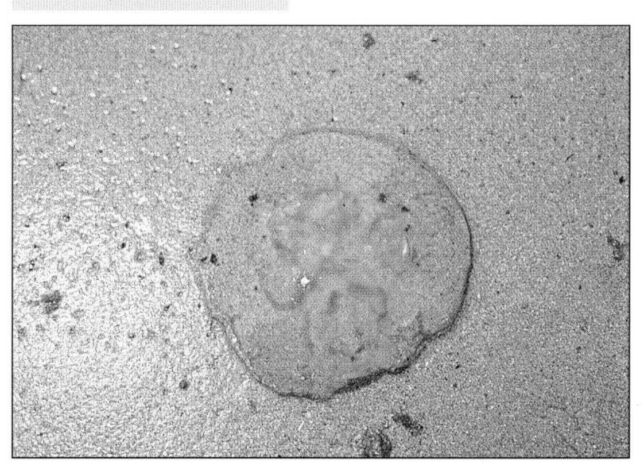

Compass Jellyfish

Chrysaora hysoscella

Smugairle an chompáis

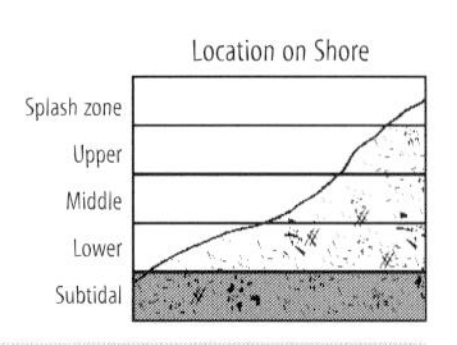

Habitat:	Floats out at sea but may be seen washed up on beaches.
Colour:	Creamy brown with dark brown markings.
Size:	Upto 3cm across with long tentacles

This jellyfish is bluish-white in colour, with brown V-shaped markings on the top of its bell-shaped body and a "frill" of brown markings around its edge. It has 24 **tentacles** that are arranged in groups, as well as four very long and "frilly" **mouth arms** and eight sense organs. Adult Compass Jellyfish are found in coastal waters from July to September, often growing up to 30cm in diameter. These can also be seen washed up the beach. The Compass Jellyfish feeds on worms and small jellyfish.

By-the-wind-sailor

Velella velella

Smugairle na gaoithe

Location on Shore

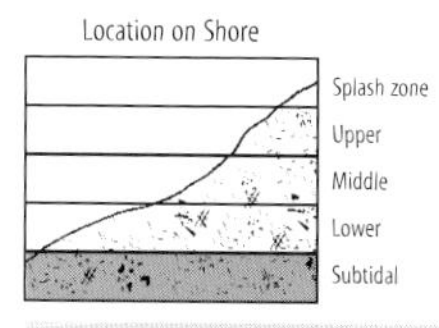

Habitat:	Floating out at sea but may be seen washed up on beaches.
Colour:	A transparent blue
Size:	Up to 10cm long

The By-the-wind-sailor is a close relative of the jellyfish. Free-floating out at sea, it has a transparent blue, oval-shaped disc that can grow up to 10cm in diameter. This disc contains a horny skeleton that encloses a float which helps keep the By-the-wind-sailor at the surface of the water. It also contains a mouth and **tentacles** underneath. On top of the skeleton is a curved, fin-like sail which catches the wind. Huge groups travel together, often washing up on beaches.

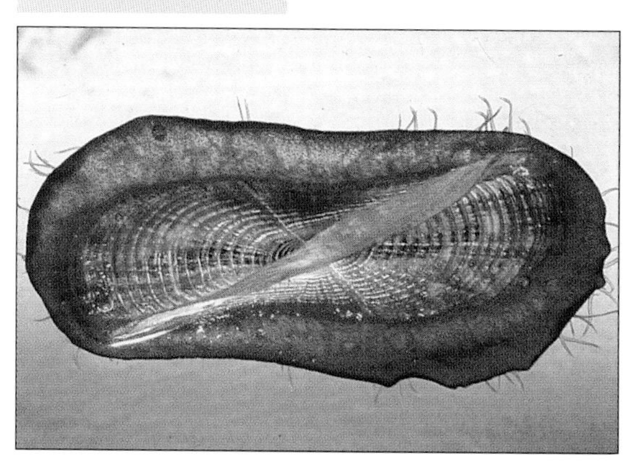

Worms

Many different kinds of worm live on the seashore and in the shallow waters around our coast. They can be found all over the shore - in mud, in sand, on or under rocks, and on other animals. Some swim or crawl in search of food. Others stay in one place for most of their lives, filtering food from the sea or collecting debris on which to feed.

The worms that live freely are called **errant** and are usually active **predators** or **scavengers**. They often have well developed eyes, **tentacles** and jaws for locating and catching food.

The worms that live in the same place for the whole of their lives are said to be **sedentary**. These worms live in a protective tube that may be buried in soft sand or mud, or cemented to a hard surface. This tube may be made of sand or mud grains stuck together with mucus, or may be formed from a limy or chalky substance secreted by the worm's body.

Some sedentary worms are **filter feeders**, using a crown of feathery tentacles to trap tiny particles of food from the water. When not feeding, or if disturbed, these tentacles can quickly be pulled inside the tube. Others use sticky tentacles to feel around on the surface of the mud or sand for particles of food.

Some typical sedentary worms

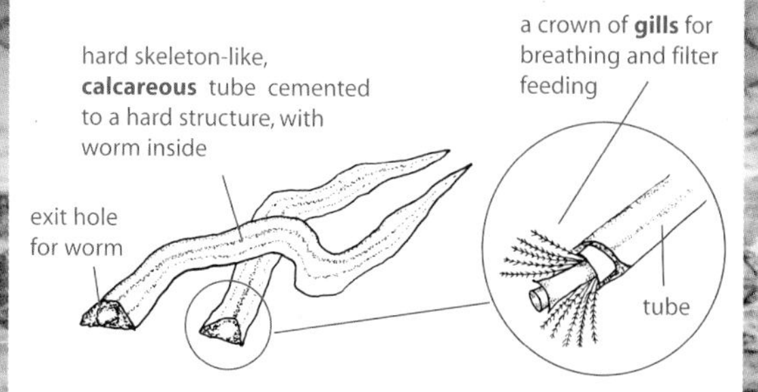

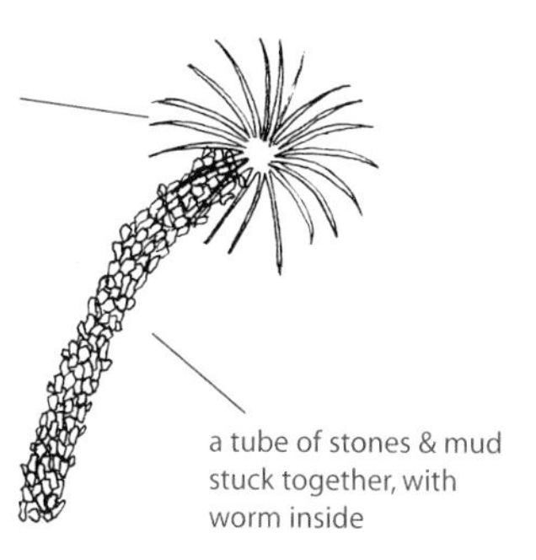

Most worms belong to a group called the polychaetes, or **bristle worms**. Within this group there are both **free-living** and sedentary species. Bristle worms are close relatives of the familiar earthworm. A close look will show that both have a body that is divided into segments. Bristle worms also have many hair-like bristles covering their body and some, such as paddleworms (page 98), have leaf-like "legs" called **parapodia**.

A typical free-living bristle worm

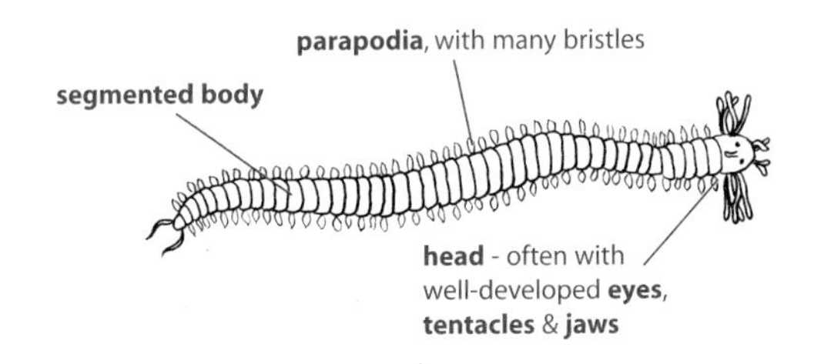

It may be difficult to get a close look at these worms. Many hide in their tubes, while others stay buried in sand or mud. Often, on muddy shores, the only evidence that they are present are the spaghetti-like mounds and holes left by **deposit feeding** worms, e.g. the lugworm (page 100). Deposit feeding occurs when the worm takes in sand and mud as it burrows, extracts the food and then passes out the undigested material in the form of a coil on the shore. This coil is known as the **cast**.

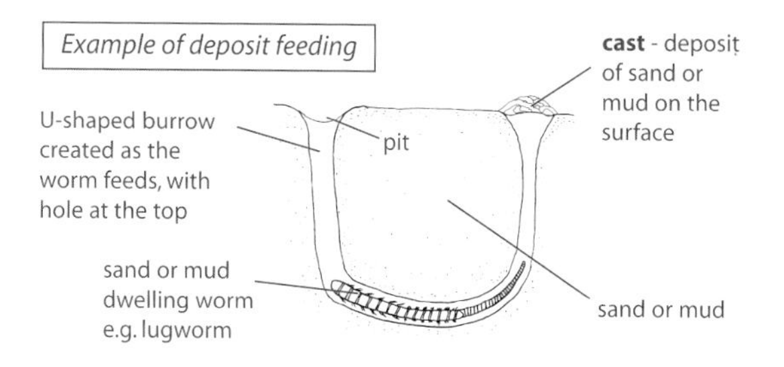

The other groups of worms include the **flatworms** and **ribbon worms**, which are both free-living. Flatworms have flat, leaf-like bodies with a pair of tiny eyes and tentacles at the front. They live mostly under rocks and among seaweeds. Ribbon worms (not featured in this book) often have extremely long, thin and unsegmented bodies. They live in mud or under rocks by day, coming out only at night to feed on other worms.

A typical flatworm

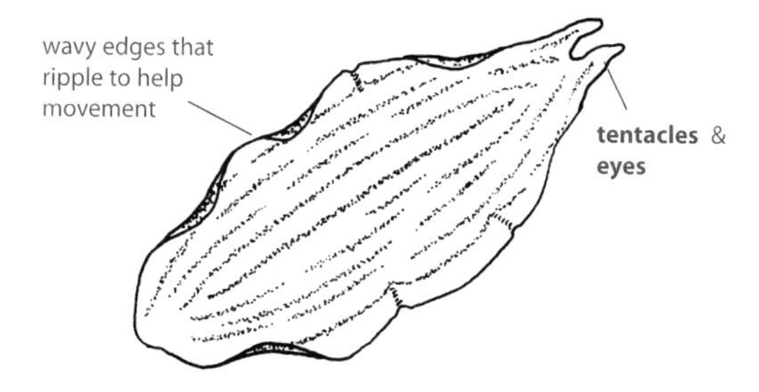

Coiled Tube Worm

Spirorbis spp.

Tiúbphéist chorntha

A very common worm on our shores, the Coiled Tube Worm, is often overlooked because of its small size. It builds a tiny **calcareous** coiled tube up to 4mm in diameter, which may be coiled clockwise or anticlockwise, depending on the species. The head bears a minute crown of green or white **gills** which are used for breathing and **filter feeding**. This worm will settle on a variety of structures, but particularly favours the **fronds** of the Serrated Wrack (page 44).

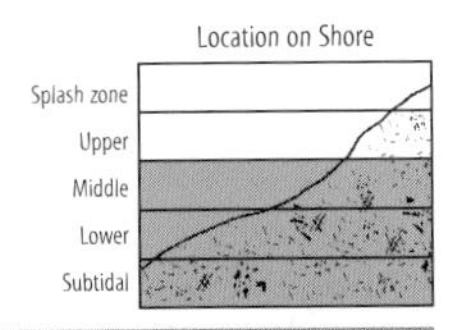

Habitat:	Encrusting on seaweed, shells & rocks
Colour:	Tube white-cream
Size:	1-4mm across

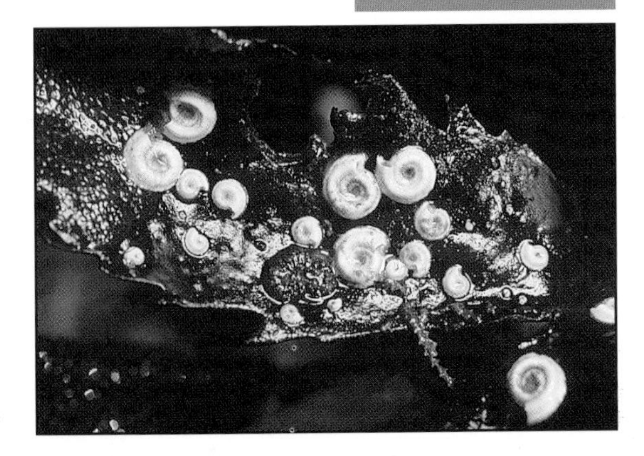

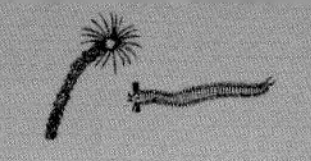

Keel Worm

Pomatoceros triqueter

Cílphéist

Location on Shore

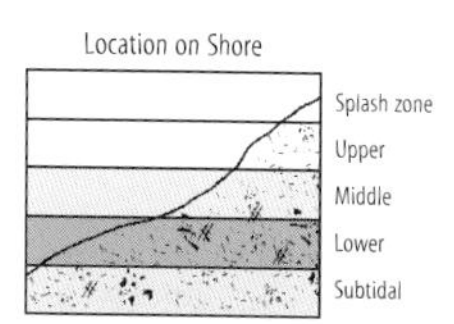

Habitat:	Encrusting on rocks, pebbles & shells on all types of shore
Colour:	White or pinkish
Size:	Up to 2.5cm

The Keel Worm lives permanently attached to hard structures, such as stones or rocks, living inside a chalky tube that it makes itself. The tube narrows to a point at the tail end and has a prominent "keel" or ridge along its length. At high tide, it puts out its head and opens out a small crown of colourful tentacle-like **gills** to catch the tiny animals and plants it feeds on. When the tide goes out, or when danger threatens, it retreats into its tube, plugging the opening with a cork formed from one of the gills.

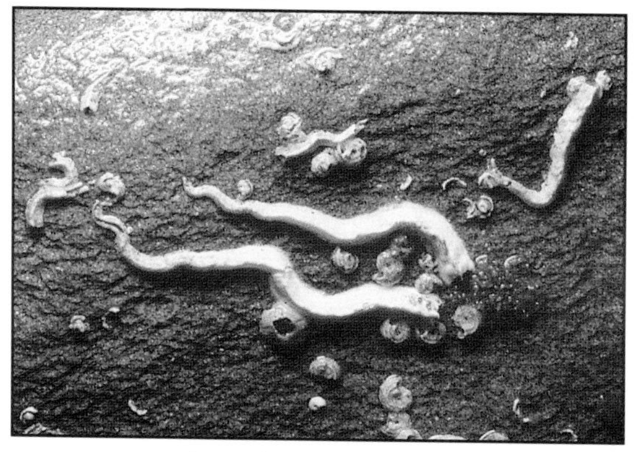

Green Leaf Worm

Eulalia viridis

Rámhach glas

The Green Leaf Worm, strikingly bright green in colour, is a member of the paddleworm family. Paddle-worms are **free-living bristle worms**. They have large leaf-like **parapodia**, which act as paddles, allowing them to swim. The small but well-developed head does not possess jaws but does have two prominent eyes and sensory **tentacles**. The Green Leaf Worm is usually seen crawling over rocks and seaweed, and often amongst mussels (page 122) and barnacles (page 150), on the lower shore.

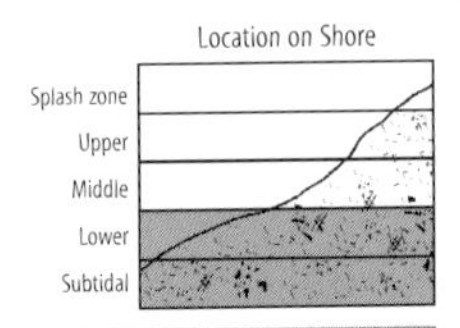

Habitat:	In crevices, under rocks & on seaweeds
Colour:	Bright green
Size:	Up to 15cm

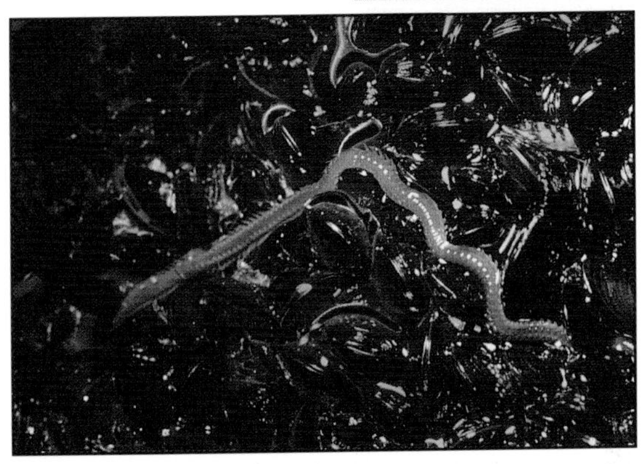

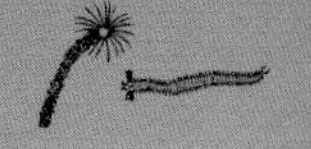

Ragworm

Hediste diversicolor
(Nereis diversicolor)

Raga

Location on Shore

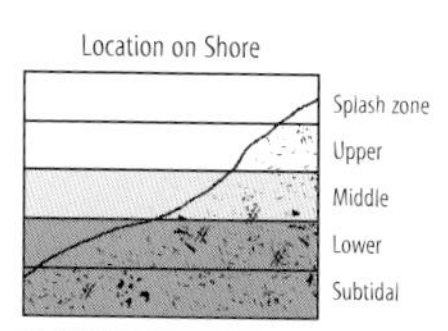

Habitat:	On soft muddy shores
Colour:	Varies from yellow green to orange red
Size:	Up to 10-12cm

The Ragworm is a fast-moving and aggressive hunter, using its strong, pincer-like jaws to catch and grip its prey. (Take care if handling it!) It eats other worms, small shrimps and anything else it can capture, as well as debris. Most Ragworms are 10-12cm long. The colour of the body can vary from yellow-green to orange-red, with a red line - the **dorsal blood vessel** - running down its back. When hunting, it can sometimes be seen on the surface of the mud, although it usually burrows down in search of food.

Lugworm

Arenicola marina

Lugach

Often the only sign of life beneath a sandy beach is the presence on the surface of spaghetti-like **casts**. A type of **bristle worm**, the Lugworm spends its life in a U-shaped burrow, feeding on the sand and extracting anything edible from it. As it feeds, a pit is formed above its head while the undigested sand is ejected as the cast. As in all bristleworms, the body is segmented and looks similar to that of the earthworm. The front of the body is swollen and bears bristles, and the narrower end bears red **gills**, which are used for breathing.

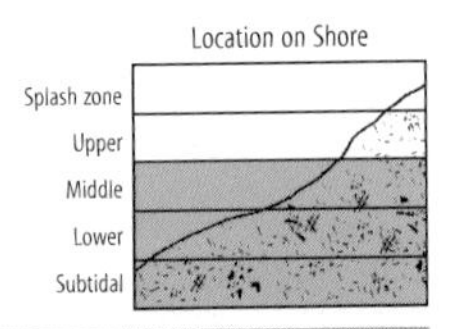

Habitat:	On muddy & sandy shores
Colour:	Dark greenish-brown
Size:	Up to 20cm

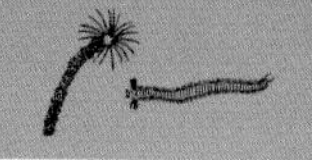

Honeycomb Worm

Sabellaria alveolata

Péist mhilteogach

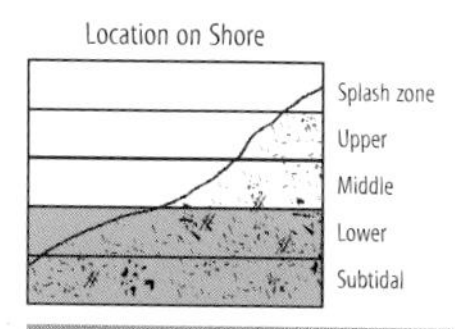

Habitat:	Encrusting rocks particularly on sandy shores
Colour:	Oatmeal, buff, orange brown
Size:	Worm up to 4cm long

Honeycomb Worms live in a group, or **colony**, often on a half-buried rock on exposed beaches. These colonies may be so big as to form large reef-like structures. They build tubes by gluing together sand grains, gravel or shell pieces, and arranging them rather like a honey-comb in a bee hive. The worms are fairly small, up to 4cm in length, and emerge only at high tide to feed. At low tide they shut them-selves in their tubes, with **tentacles** adapted to form a plug-like structure.

Sand Mason

Lanice conchilega

Péist fheadáin trá

A tube sticking up from the sand and built of sand grains is home to the Sand Mason. The top of the tube is decorated with a mop of branched structures, also made out of sand. These help protect delicate and sticky **tentacles** that wave about in the water, trapping the tiny food particles that are present. This food is then passed to the mouth. In between the tentacles there are six scarlet branching **gills**, which may be seen when the worm is closely observed.

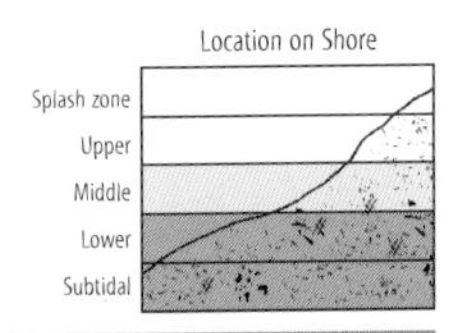

Habitat:	On sand & gravel shores
Colour:	Yellowish, pink or brown
Size:	Up to 30cm

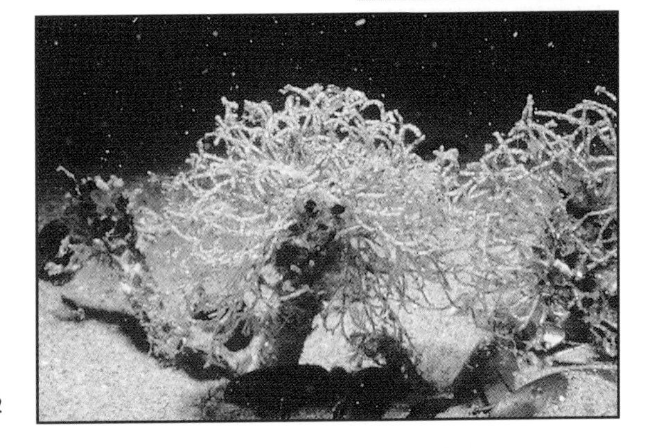

Peacock Worm

Sabella pavonina

Péist phéacóige

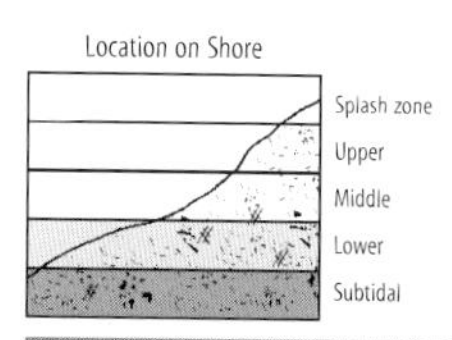

Habitat:	In mud & sand
Colour:	Varied - fan often beautifully patterned & brightly coloured
Size:	Tube length 25cm

The Peacock Worm is a worm that lives in a narrow tube made out of mud particles glued together with mucus. This tube can often reach 25cm in length. When covered by seawater, the worm emerges from its tube and sticks out a spectacular circular fan of multicoloured, feathery **gills**. These filter tiny animals and plants from the water and waft them down to its mouth. If the worm is disturbed while feeding, the fan is rapidly pulled back into the tube.

Sea Mouse

Aphrodita aculeata

Luch mhara

The Sea Mouse is a most unlikely-looking worm. The short, stout, oval-shaped body is covered with a "fur" of brownish-grey hairs, which may be matted with mud. Its dull appearance is brightened by longer, golden-brown and greenish bristles along the sides which can take on an **iridescent** sheen. Although usually found below the low tide mark, it is somtimes found ploughing its way through mud on the lower shore, where it has probably been washed up after storms.

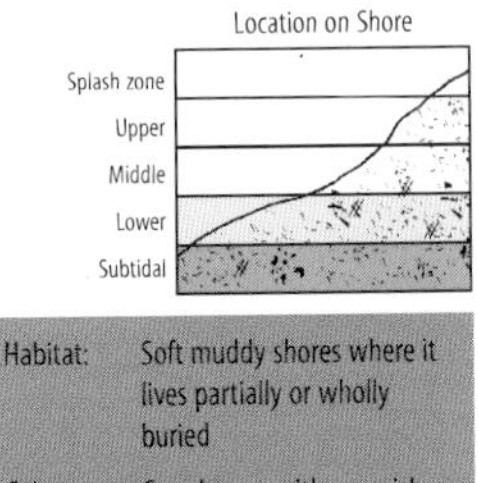

Habitat:	Soft muddy shores where it lives partially or wholly buried
Colour:	Grey-brown with greenish-gold irridescence
Size:	10cm-20cm

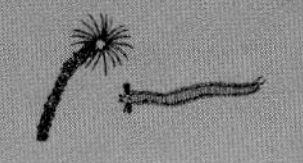

Candy-stripe Worm

Prosthecaraeus vittatus

Leithphéist stríoca candaí

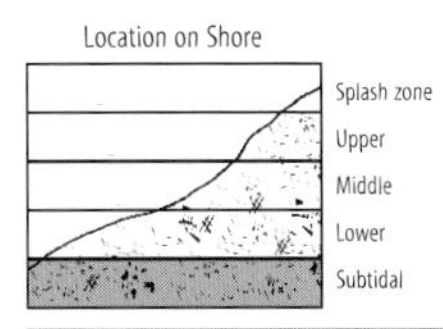

Habitat:	Under stones in mud
Colour:	Cream with brown stripes
Size:	Up to 5cm

The Candy-stripe Worm is a flatworm that has a flat, broad body which narrows towards the tail end. The wavy edges of the body can be rippled to help movement. On the head there are **tentacles** and groups of dark brown eye spots. It is creamish-white in colour and has dark brown stripes running down the length of its body. This **flatworm** can grow up to 5cm in length and lives under stones in the mud.

Shells & Relatives

The shells we find washed up on the beach have most likely been made by an animal called a **mollusc**. Most molluscs have a soft, fleshy body, a strong, muscular **foot** and a hard, limy shell on the outside for protection. In some molluscs, however, the shell is inside the body or is completely absent. The shell is secreted by the body of the mollusc and it increases in size as the body grows.

Some molluscs make a single shell which is often, but not always, coiled into a spiral. These molluscs are called **gastropods** and this group includes both land snails and sea snails.

The shell of a gastropod has a single opening through which the muscular foot comes out. This foot is very useful. It may be used as a suction disc to prevent the animal being washed off the rocks, or as a spade for burrowing into sand or mud. It is more likely, however, that when you find a gastropod the foot will have been pulled inside the shell and, in many cases, the hole will be covered with a horny disc. This disc is called the **operculum**; it stops the animal drying out when out of water and also gives it protection.

When the tide is out, most sea snails hide away under rocks and seaweed or bury themselves in the sand and mud. When the tide comes back, in they start searching for food. Many of the sea snails found on the shore are

Some typical gastropods or sea snails

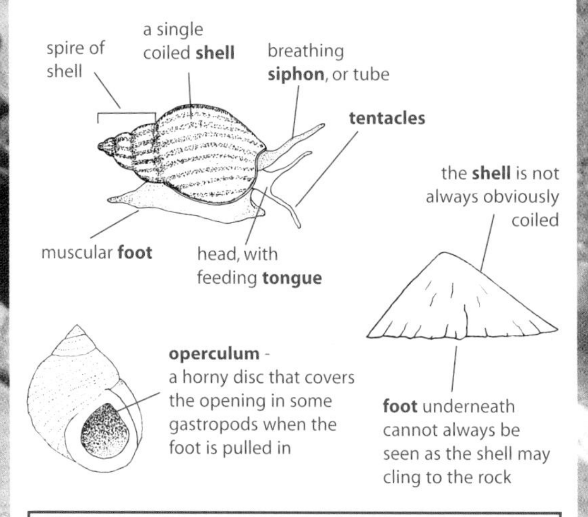

Note: There is one type of "shell" that grows on rocks and on other animals that you might expect to find in this chapter - that is that of the barnacle. The barnacle is actually another type of animal and belongs in the "Crabs & Relatives" group (page 150).

herbivores, which eat plants only. They strip tiny seaweeds off the rock with a tongue that is covered in teeth. Others are active **predators** feeding on worms, barnacles and other animals. Some are even able to drill through the shells of other molluscs to get at the flesh inside.

Molluscs can have more than one shell. Those that have two shells joined together are called **bivalves**. The two shells, which are known as **valves**, are joined by a strong hinge-like **ligament**, which keep the shells together as they open and close. The shells also have powerful muscles inside which help keep them tightly shut.

Bivalves usually live buried in sand or mud, using their muscular foot to dig downwards. When open, they feed and breathe by extending two short tubes up to the surface. They draw water and particles into their shell through one of the tubes, called the **inhalent siphon**, and pass it over feather-like **gills**. These gills absorb the oxygen and filter out the tiny food particles. The water is then pumped out of the shell through the second tube, called the **exhalent siphon**. This type of feeding is called **filter feeding**.

Because bivalves only breathe and feed when covered by water, they must remain closed when the tide goes out and must wait until the water covers them again before they can breathe or eat.

Some bivalves, such as oysters and mussels, never move from one spot. They attach themselves firmly to rocks or other solid structures, using cement or strong

Some typical bivalves

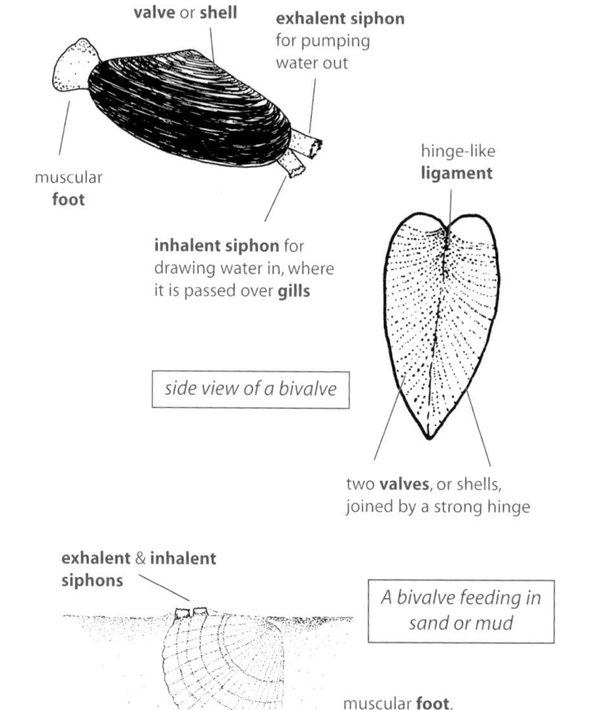

side view of a bivalve

A bivalve feeding in sand or mud

threads, called **byssus threads**. They also have inhalent and exhalent siphons, which are not as obvious. Not living directly in sand or mud, they feed more on particles in the water and are also known as **filter feeders**.

A typical chiton

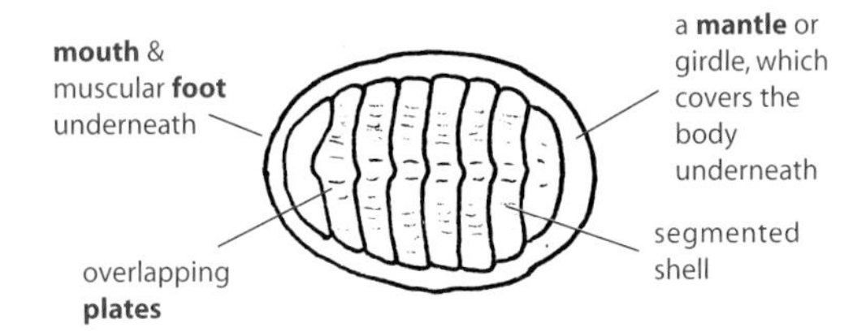

A few bivalves, such as scallops (page 129), are able to swim freely by opening and closing their shells and forcing out a jet of water. This form of "jet propulsion" is useful for escaping from predators.

There is one family of molluscs that has more than two shells. These are called **chitons** or Coat-of-mail shells. They might have as many as eight parts to their shell and they can curl up into a ball like a woodlouse. Chitons creep slowly over the rocks in search of microscopic plants on which to feed.

Not all molluscs have obvious shells. **Sea slugs**, which usually live offshore, can sometimes been seen on the shore during the spring and summer, when they come there to have their young. Some sea slugs have a shell hidden inside their body, and others have no shell at all. Because sea slugs have no protective shell, many use camouflage and give off chemicals to turn away attackers. Unlike their dull cousins on land, they often have brightly-coloured tentacles on their head and colourful "frills" along their body. These "frills" are actually **gills** that they use for breathing underwater.

A typical sea slug

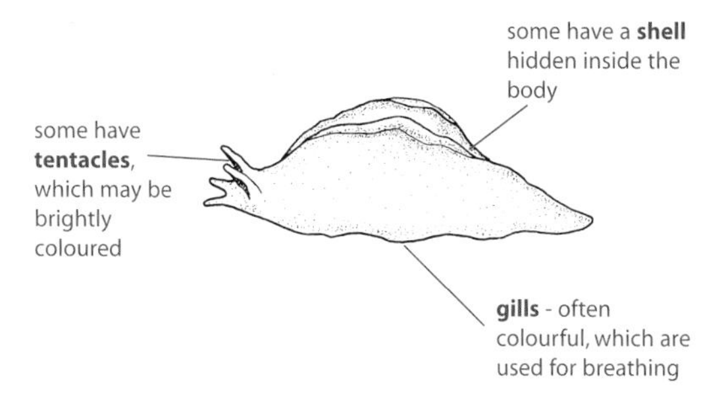

Common Limpet

Patella vulgata

Bairneach coiteann

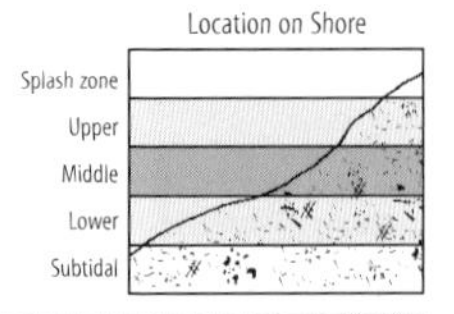

Habitat:	On rocky shores
Colour:	Grey shell; whitish inside with brown scar; foot olive-green
Size:	Up to 7cm long

Easily recognised by its cone-shaped shell, the Common Limpet is a familiar sight on rocky shores. With a strong sucker **foot**, it is an expert at clinging to the rock surface. This watertight grip helps the limpet keep water in its shell and also protects it from strong waves and **predators**. Each limpet has a "home base" on a rock - an oval scar which is the exact shape of the shell. When covered by water, the limpet wanders over the rock surface, grazing on tiny seaweeds and on **encrusting animals**, returning to the scar when the tide goes out again.

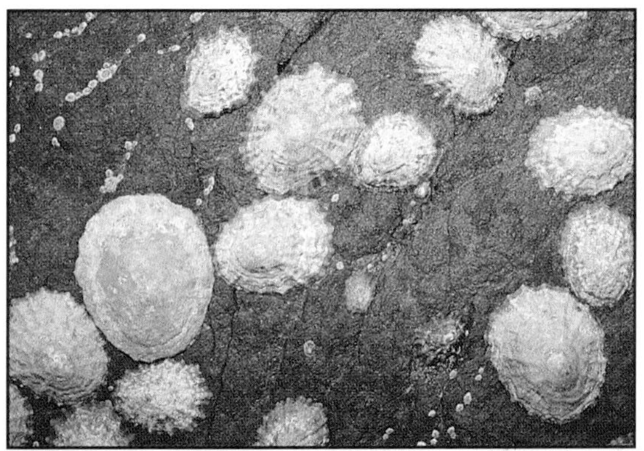

Edible Periwinkle

Littorina littorea

Gioradán

Location on Shore

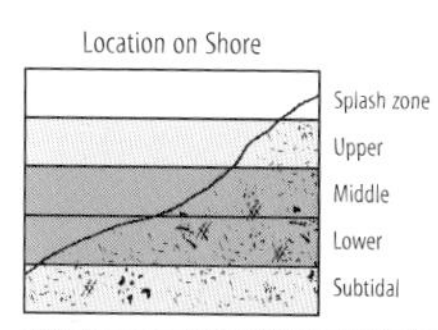

Habitat:	On rocky shores, often under seaweed
Colour:	Usually a dull grey-brown
Size:	Up to 3cm

The Edible Periwinkle is one of the most familiar sea snails on the seashore and is the largest of the winkle family. It has a thick coiled shell, which is dark grey-brown in colour, often with darker lines. This colouring helps it to blend in with the seaweeds under which it lives. When out of water, the Edible Periwinkle closes its shell with a horny disc called the **operculum**, sealing the animal inside. This periwinkle is found on all types of shore.

Flat Periwinkle

Littorina obtusata
(Littorina littoralis)
Faocha leathan

This sea snail is commonly found on the middle to lower shore, grazing on many of the large brown seaweeds, especially the wracks (page 41-45). It ranges in colour from bright yellow to brown, through to red, green and orange. It may also be banded. The Flat Periwinkle, which is quite smooth, is usually very small, reaching only 1cm in height. It gets its common name from the flat, rounded shape of the top of the shell.

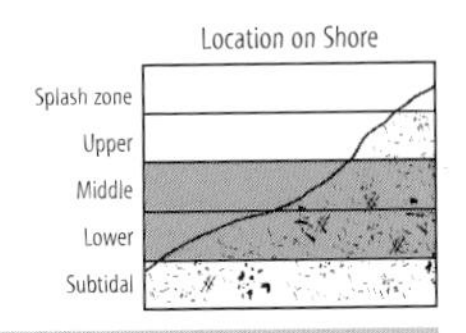

Habitat:	On rocky shores, often on larger brown seaweeds
Colour:	Brown, red, green, yellow or orange - sometimes banded
Size:	Up to 1cm

Rough Periwinkle

Littorina saxatilis

Faocha gharbh

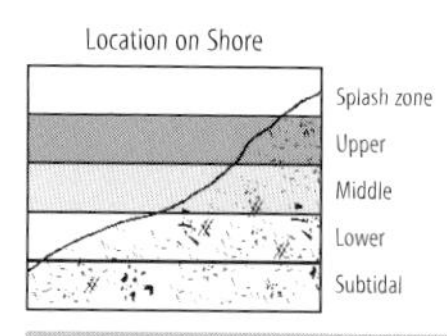

Habitat:	On rocky shores, often in crevices
Colour:	Brown, red, green, yellow orange or black
Size:	Up to 1.8cm

As its name suggests, the Rough Periwinkle is rough to the touch. It has a grooved shell that is pointed at the top. Generally small in size, it can grow up to 1.8cm high. Its colour can vary, but is usually orange-red or black, often appearing faded grey. It is found on rocks and in crevices on the upper and middle shore. A similar, but much smaller and darker periwinkle, is *Littorina neritoides*. This tiny shell is also found on the upper shore, in crevices and often in dead barnacles (page 150).

Dogwhelk

Nucella lapillus

Cuachma chon

The Dogwhelk is a common sea snail found on rocky shores, often in large numbers, from the middle shore to shallow water. Its colour can vary, but is usually a grey/cream and often marked or patterned with dark brown bands. It lays its eggs on the seashore, usually in crevices and under seaweed from the middle shore down (see inset). The eggs can be found in large groups and look like yellowy brown grains of rice standing on end.

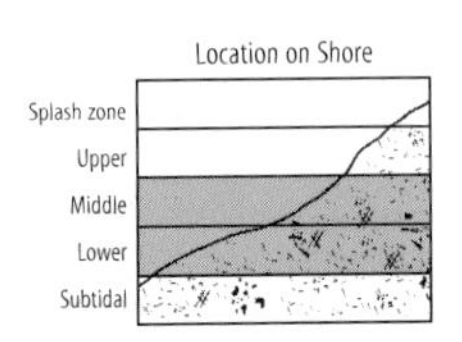

Habitat:	On rocky shores
Colour:	Cream-grey to white, sometimes white with brown stripes
Size:	Up to 4cm long

Painted Topshell

Calliostoma zizyphinum

Faochán Mhuire dathannach

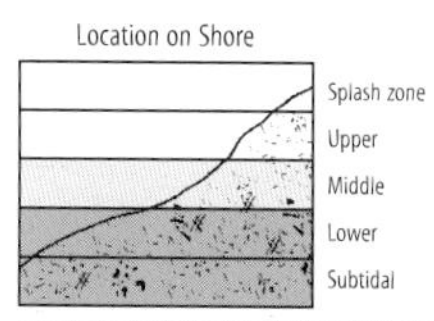

Habitat:	On rocky shores, especially under seaweed
Colour:	Shell usually salmon pink, with darker banding & white spots
Size:	Up to 3cm high

One of the most colourful shells to be found on the rocky shore, the Painted Topshell, has a coiled, cone-shaped shell. Its common name comes from its resemblance to the old-fashioned spinning tops with which children used to play. The shell is usually a salmon-pink, colour, with dark red bands and white spots. However, shells that are all white do occur. The animal itself has a bright yellow-pink **foot**; when that is fully withdrawn into the shell, the opening is closed by a horny disc called the **operculum**.

Thick/Toothed Topshell

Osilinus lineatus

(Monodonta lineata)

Faochán Mhuire tiubh

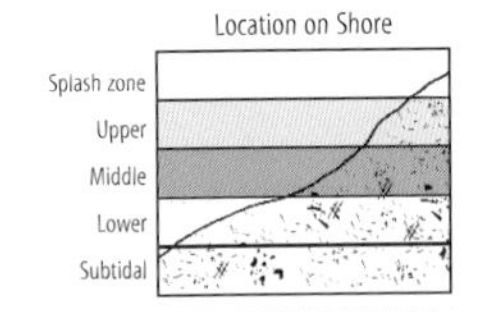

Habitat:	On rocky shores
Colour:	Grey-green, with purple zig-zags
Size:	2-3cm high

The Thick Topshell can grow up to 3cm in diameter and in height. It is grey-green in colour, with purple zig-zags. Sometimes, the top of the shell may be worn away and appear yellow. Identifying features are a **"tooth"** near the shell opening, and a beautiful mother-of-pearl appearance inside the shell. Living on the middle shore, it feeds on seaweeds, and, like many sea snails, it has to survive periods of drought. It uses a horny disc, called the **operculum**, to seal the animal inside the shell when out of water.

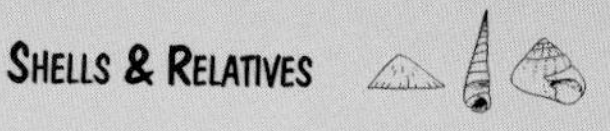

Purple/Flat Topshell

Gibbula umbilicalis

Faochán Mhuire corcra

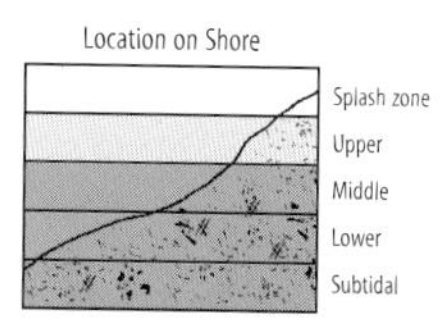

Habitat:	On rocky shores
Colour:	Silvery green-grey, with purple markings
Size:	Up to 2cm

The Purple Topshell is smaller and flatter than the Thick Topshell (page 118), growing to about 2cm in diameter. It has a silvery grey-green shell with purple bands. It is usually found under stones and feeding on seaweeds, from the middle shore down to shallow water. It can also be found in rockpools on the upper shore. It is very similar to the Grey Topshell, *Gibbula cineraria*, but its shell is a little flatter and has stronger markings.

European Cowrie

Trivia monacha

Fínicín Eorpach

This **gastropod** has a small, oval, egg-shaped shell that can grow up to 1.2cm in width. It has a ribbed surface and a slit-like opening on its flattened underside. Its colour varies, ranging from cream to pink-orange to brown, with 3 brown spots on top. The underside is usually paler in colour than the upper surface. It lives on the lower shore, and in shallow waters on rocky shores, where it feeds on Star Ascidians (page 74). However, the empty shells of European Cowries are often wash up on beaches.

Location on Shore

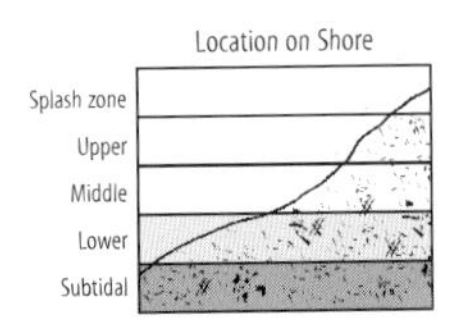

Habitat:	On rocky shores, in shallow water & can be washed ashore
Colour:	Cream to pink-orange to brown
Size:	Up to 1.2cm

Blue-rayed Limpet

Helcion pellucidum
(Patina pellucida)
Bairneach mín

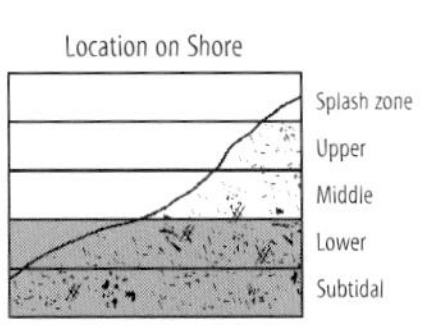

Habitat:	Attached to fronds & stems of kelp seaweeds, often washed ashore
Colour:	Orange brown with electric blue lines when young
Size:	Up to 1.5cm

Often found attached to the **fronds** of kelp seaweeds (page 46-47), this sea snail's body is covered by a single uncoiled shell. When young, the shell is smooth and orange-brown in colour with broken electric blue lines running down its length. With age, its colour fades to a dull brown, with darker banding and grey lines. The Blue-rayed Limpet normally feeds on kelps, but also feeds on **encrusting animals** or plants. Oval scars on the fronds and stems of kelps are "home bases" to which the limpet returns after feeding.

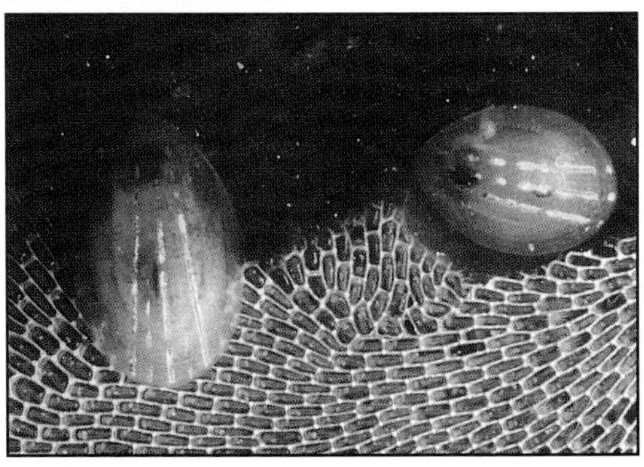

Common/Blue Mussel

Mytilus edulis

Diúilicín

This **bivalve mollusc** prefers to attach itself to a hard structure. Its shell is slightly oval shaped and may be blue, black or brown in colour. Inside, it is pearly white with a darker, blueish-black border. Mussels often live together in huge beds, in areas where there is plenty of water movement. The water carries tiny animals and plants which the mussel filters out, using its **gills**. It attaches itself to stones, rocks and to other mussels, using strong hair-like **byssus threads**.

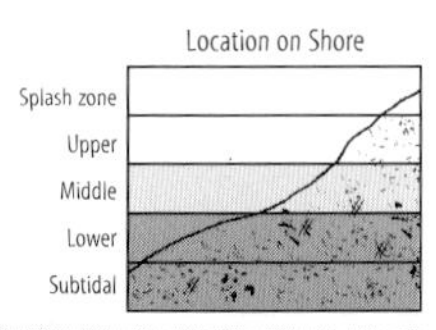

Habitat:	Attached to rocks & stones on rocky shores
Colour:	Blue black or brown shell, pearly white inside with darker border
Size:	1-10cm in length

Common Saddle Oyster

Anomia ephippium

Sligín slámach

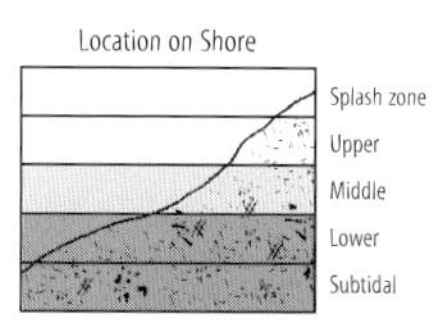

Habitat:	Attached to rocks, stones, seaweeds & other shells
Colour:	White or pale brown, pearly inside
Size:	Upto 6cm across

This is one of the few **bivalve molluscs** that do not live buried in sand or mud. The upper half of the shell is cemented to rocks by hard, chalky **byssus threads** that grow through a hole in the lower shell, or **valve**. The shell is quite flat and circular. However, it is sometimes distorted, as it takes the shape of whatever it is attached to. At first, the shell is quite thin but it increases in thickness with age. The interior is usually white with a pearly sheen, while the exterior is white or pale brown.

Common/Edible Cockle

Cerastoderma edule
(Cardium edule)

Ruacan

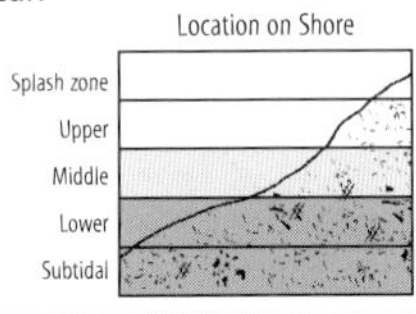

Habitat:	Buried in sand or sandy mud, often washed up
Colour:	Greyish-white, sometimes with darker brown marks
Size:	Up to 5cm long

The Common Cockle is a **bivalve** that lives buried in sand or mud, from the middle shore down. Its empty shell is often all that is seen on the surface. The thick shell is greyish-white in colour and has broad, rounded ribs that run from the top to the edge of the shell. Running across these are growth rings which show the animal's age, each heavy ring equalling a year. The cockle lives 2-3cm below the surface, anchored by its **foot**. When the tide is in, it pushes its two tube-like **siphons** to the surface of the sand to feed and breathe.

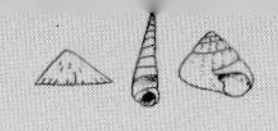

Banded Wedge Shell

Donax vittatus

Sliogán dinge bandach

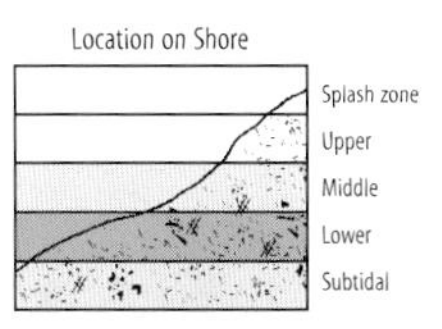

Habitat:	Burrowing in sand, in shallow water & often washed up
Colour:	Whitish, can be banded cream, orange & brown - often purple inside
Size:	Up to 3.8cm long

Each shell of this small **bivalve** has a side which is much shorter than the other, forming a sort of wedge. The outside of the shell is banded and varies in colour, most commonly being white, orange, brown and purple. It can be recognised by the violet-blue colouring on the inside of the shell and by the saw-like inner edge. The Banded Wedge Shell lives buried in sand on the shore and in shallow water. Its empty shell is particularly common on fairly exposed shores and, despite being small, is quite tough.

A **bivalve**, the Blunt Tellin has an oval-shaped and thick creamy shell, with bands running across it. The two halves, or **valves**, of the shell are held together by a strong brown **ligament**. It is usual to find only one empty shell on the beach as they usually live buried in the sand or mud. The Blunt Tellin has a large **foot** which allows it to burrow quickly into sand if it is uncovered by the tide. This **filter feeder** has two **siphons** which it uses rather like a vacuum cleaner to suck up food that is lying on the surface of the sand.

Banded Carpet Shell

Tapes rhomboides

(Paphia/Venerupis rhomboides)

Breallach croise bandach

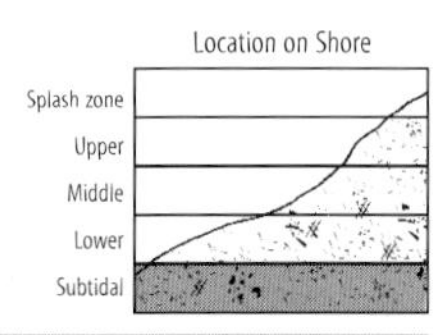

Habitat:	Buried in muddy, sandy or gravel shores
Colour:	White, cream, yellow or orange
Size:	Up to 6cm

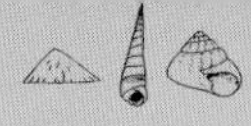
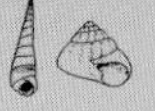

Common/Curved Razor Shell

Ensis ensis

Scian mhara chuar

Location on Shore

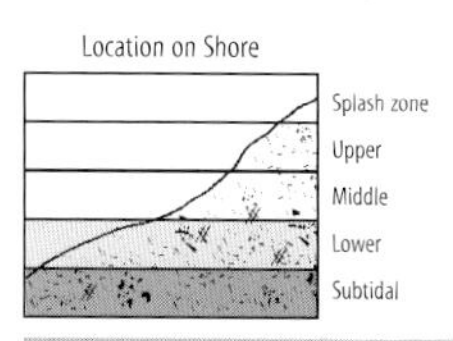

Habitat:	Burrowing in sand, often washed ashore
Colour:	White but often covered with brownish horny covering
Size:	Up to 12cm

This **bivalve** has a long thin, slightly curved, rectangular shell, which is sometimes found empty on the shore. The two halves, or **valves**, of the shell are held together by a strong **ligament** along one side. When the shell is closed, the ends remain open, creating a tube-like effect. It is a **filter feeder** and must remain close to the surface, as its **siphon** is very short. If disturbed, it can rapidly pull itself deeper into the sand by extending its strong, muscular **foot**, which it uses to pull its shell downwards.

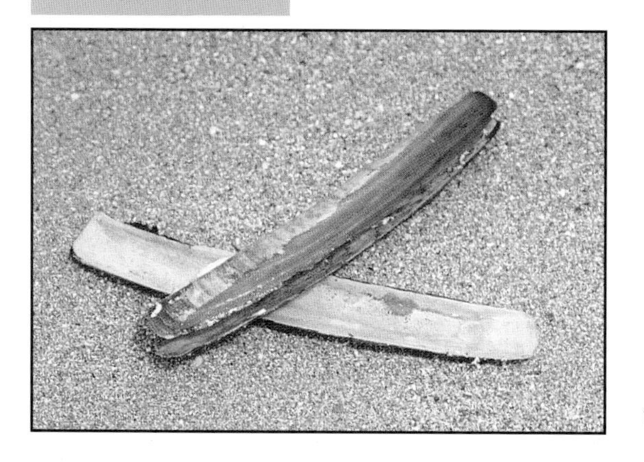

Common Otter Shell

Lutraria lutraria

Sliogán dobharchú coiteann

The Common Otter Shell is a **bivalve** and is difficult to find alive, as it usually burrows 20-23cm into the sand or mud on the extreme lower shore. It is commonly found washed up on sandy and muddy beaches. Its smooth and oval-shaped shell is made up of two slightly cupped **valves**, joined by a strong hinge-like **ligament**. It can grow to 12cm in width and is yellowish-white, often with a brownish, horny covering. It has a very long **siphon** that it uses to reach the surface, to draw in food.

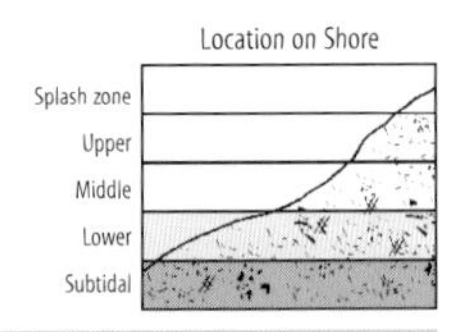

Habitat:	On muddy, sandy or gravelly shores
Colour:	Yellowish-white with brown covering
Size:	Up to 12cm

Great Scallop

Pecten maximus

Muirín mór

Location on Shore

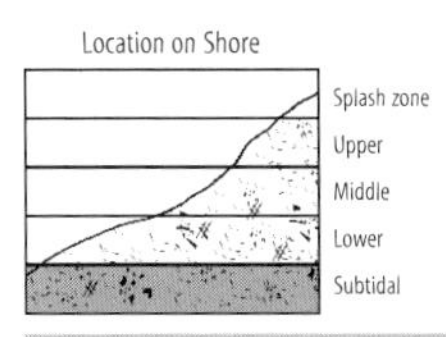

Habitat:	On sandy & gravelly shores, often washed up
Colour:	Reddish-brown with white markings
Size:	Up to 15cm across

The Great Scallop is a large **bivalve mollusc**. It has a thick, almost circular shell, made up of two **valves** joined together with a strong hinge-like **ligament**. The bottom valve is deeply cupped, while the upper valve is flat. Both have deep grooves or ribs that radiate down the shell. It is reddish-brown with white markings and can grow up to 15cm in diameter. An active swimmer, it is commonly found in fine sand or gravel in offshore waters, but the empty shell is often washed on to beaches.

Coat-of-mail Chiton

Lepidochitona cinerea

Ciotón máille

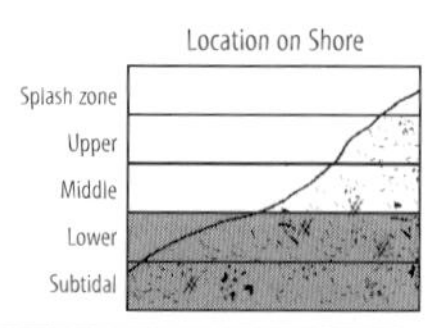

Habitat:	Attached to rocks & other hard surfaces
Colour:	Shell green, grey or brown; body appears grainy
Size:	Up to 2cm

This little **mollusc** is common on rocky shores. It lives attached to the rock and is well camouflaged. Its body, which looks similar to that of a woodlouse, is protected by a shell made up of eight overlapping **plates**. This jointed shell allows the Chiton to cling snugly to rocks and to roll up into a protective ball if the animal is dislodged. Its fleshy edges and a broad **foot** underneath, act like a suction pad, anchoring it to the rock surface. The Chiton feeds by **rasping** tiny seaweeds off the rock with its tongue, which bears minute teeth.

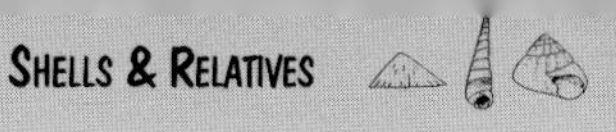

Sea Hare

Aplysia punctata

Giorria mara

Location on Shore

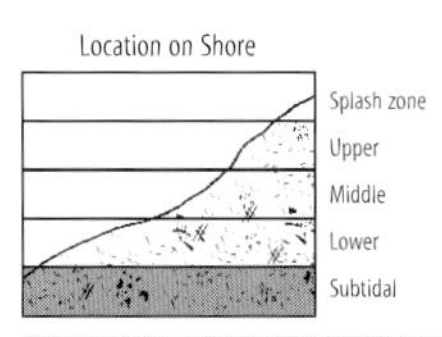

Habitat:	Among seaweeds in shallow water
Colour:	Reddish to brownish-green to black
Size:	Upto 20cm long

The Sea Hare may seem an unlikely member of the **mollusc** group, as it has no obvious shell. Its shell, however, is almost hidden by its body, which is small and flat and can grow up to 14cm in length. Reddish in colour when young, it often lives among red seaweeds in shallow water. However, this colour changes to a brownish-green when it becomes an adult. It has four **tentacles** on its head, and gets its name from the two flattened tentacles which look like the ears of a hare. If disturbed, it may fire out a purple dye.

Crabs & Relatives

Crabs and shrimps belong to a large group of animals known as **crustaceans**. These animals usually have a hard, shell-like skeleton. The shell that covers the body is called a **carapace**, and this protects the soft parts inside. The body is made up of the head, **thorax** (the middle part of the body) and **abdomen** (the stomach). Though the body of the crustacean is segmented, this is more obvious in such animals as the shrimp and prawn.

Crustaceans have jointed legs. Those that have five pairs of legs belong to a group known as **decapods** (meaning ten legs). This group includes crabs, squat lobsters, shrimp and prawns.

Most crustaceans are free-living and can be found moving about on the shore and in rockpools. Some, like crabs, squat lobsters and sandhoppers, can survive out of water for certain periods while others, such as prawns and shrimp, need to be in water permanently.

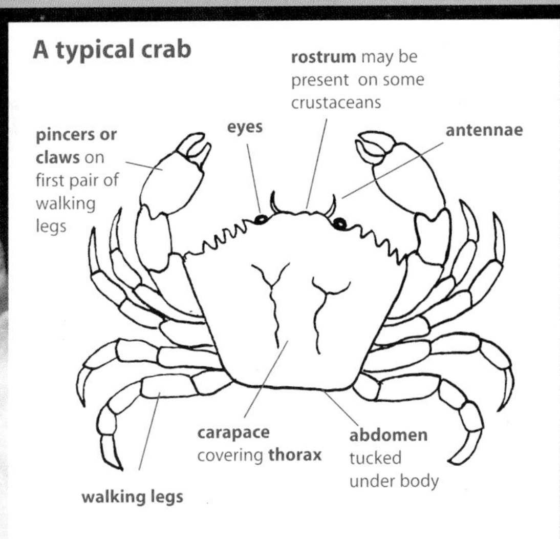

Probably one of the most exciting crustaceans found on the seashore is the **crab**. In the crab, the carapace, which covers the thorax, is usually rounded. The abdomen is not easy to see, as it is quite small and is folded underneath the body. The crab's head contains strong jaws and a pair of eyes. Between these are **antennae**, which are used for feeling. In some cases the carapace forms a point, called the **rostrum**, which helps protect the crabs head.

The crab has five pairs of walking legs, which are jointed to help movement. The first pair of legs bears large

pincers or **claws**. These are used for defence, feeding, and in some species for courtship display. They are also very strong and powerful, so be careful! Although crabs walk, most can walk sideways only. In certain species, such as the Velvet Swimming Crab (page 139), the back legs have been adapted for swimming. These legs have become flattened and act like paddles.

Crabs are **scavengers** and eat decaying flesh. They are also **predators**, eating small animals and even other crabs. But crabs can also be eaten by larger animals, and many therefore hide under rocks and seaweeds. They have also developed colouring that helps them blend in with the background on the shore.

For crabs to grow, they must shed their hard "shell" from time to time. This is known as moulting. Before shedding the old shell, the crab grows a new, soft shell underneath. Once the old shell has been shed, the animal absorbs water and swells up. The new shell expands and hardens, allowing the crab room to grow.

It is possible to tell whether a crab is male or female by looking at the width of the abdomen. In male crabs, the abdomen is a narrow triangular flap underneath the thorax, while in the female it is much broader. Sometimes you may see the female crab carrying her eggs underneath her body, between the abdomen and the thorax. These appear as an orange coloured mass.

The other decapods, the **shrimp**, **prawns** and **squat lobsters**, are different from the crab in that the abdomen is longer and sometimes extends behind the animal like a

A typical shrimp

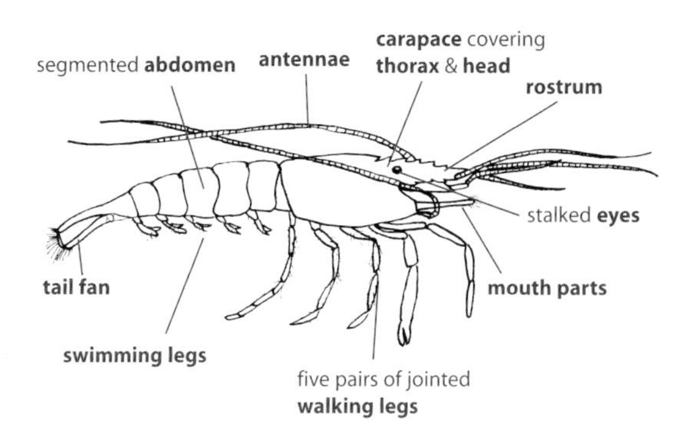

tail. It is also quite easy to see the segmented body, which is one of the main features of a crustacean.

Although the first walking legs of the squat lobster also bear large pincers like those of the crab, the shrimp and prawns found in rockpools have very small pincers. They have many legs, some of which are used for swimming and others for walking and feeding.

As with crabs, prawns and shrimp also have eyes on stalks, a rostrum and long antennae. The rostrum is quite prominent on the prawn and is often used to identify the different species.

There are two other crustaceans with features similar to those of the prawns and shrimp, but which belong to different groups. **Sea slaters** look very like woodlice. They live on the upper part of the shore, hiding during the day and feeding by night. The **sandhopper** is a tiny crustacean that lives on sandy or muddy beaches and looks like a flattened, curled up shrimp.

A typical sea slater

A typical sandhopper

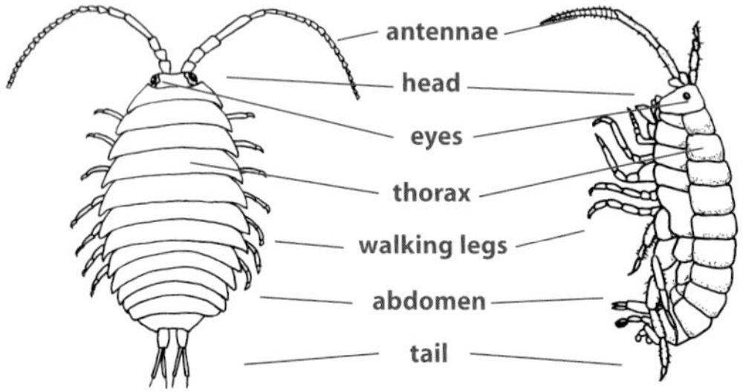

antennae
head
eyes
thorax
walking legs
abdomen
tail

At first glance you might think that **barnacles** are shells and belong in the chapter called "Shells and Relatives". Although they may not look like the other crustaceans we have just talked about, they do belong here in this group. They are not **free-living** but spend their adult life stuck to rocks or other hard surfaces, often forming thick blankets of cover.

A typical barnacle

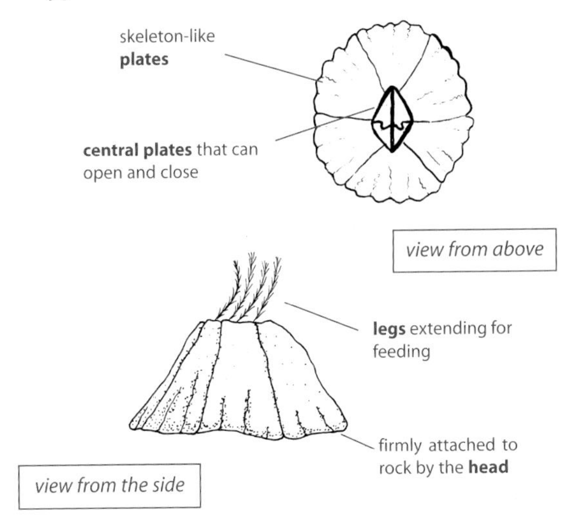

If you look very closely with your magnifying glass, you can see that the animal is protected by a chalky "shell" made up of **plates**. The animal is actually living upside down, with an opening in the centre that is covered by small plates. When tightly closed, it protects the animal inside and stops it drying out when uncovered by water for long periods. The barnacle feeds in water by opening the centre plates, extending its legs to feed on the tiny particles present.

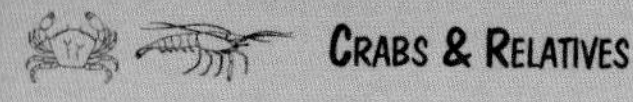

Common Shore Crab

Carcinus maenas

Portán glas

This is the most common of all the crabs found on the shore. Its has a mottled appearance, its colour varying from yellows to reds through browns and greens to black. These colours provide perfect camouflage amongst the seaweeds on the shore. The front of the **carapace** is deeply serrated like a saw and is much broader than the back. The Common Shore Crab is found under rocks and seaweed, on rocky and sandy shores and in shallow waters.

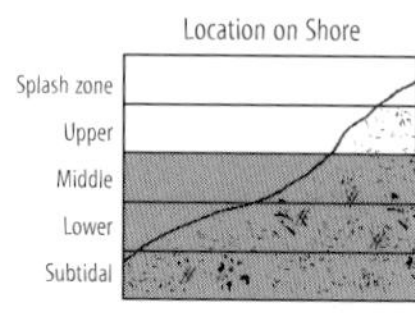

Habitat:	On rocky & sandy shores, often under rocks & seaweed & in shallow waters
Colour:	Mottled green or brown, yellow or red or even black
Size:	Carapace up to 6cm across

Velvet Swimming Crab

Necora puber
(Macropipus puber)
Luaineachán

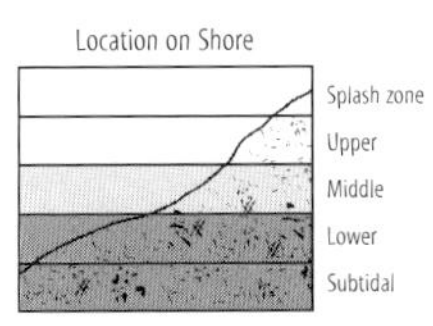

Habitat:	On rocky shores
Colour:	Grey brown with red eyes, blue joints & lines on legs
Size:	Carapace up to 8cm across

This crab gets its name from the velvet feel of its shell, and its paddle-like back legs, which are used for swimming. Its bright, red eyes and aggressive nature have earned it the nickname "red-eyed devil". The hairy **carapace** is wider at the front than at the back. The front edge is also deeply toothed, giving it a saw-like appearance. Usually dark grey to brown in colour, features to look out for are the dark blue-black lines on its legs and bright blue joints.

Edible Crab

Cancer pagurus

Portán dearg

It is easy to recognise this red-brown crab, with the "pie crust" edging of its **carapace**, its small green eyes, and the black tips on its large **pincers**. These claws, which are used for defence and feeding, tend to be bigger on the male than on the female. The edible crab can tuck its legs underneath its body and partly bury itself among stones and pebbles, making it difficult to see. Those found on the shore are usually small, but much larger specimens are found in deep waters.

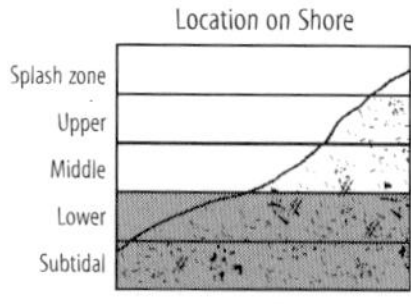

Habitat:	On rocky & gravel shores & in rockpools
Colour:	Red brown with green eyes and back tipped claws
Size:	Carapace up to 25cm across

Xantho incisus

Xantho incisus is a relatively small crab, with a broad **carapace** only about 7cm across. Its surface is smooth, with a knobbly appearance. It ranges in colour from yellow, through green to reddish-brown. It has large, dark-tipped **pincers** which can vary slightly in size, even on the same crab. Other legs become smaller towards the rear and have few hairs. It can be found on the lower shore, and in shallow water among stones or on sand or gravel.

Location on Shore

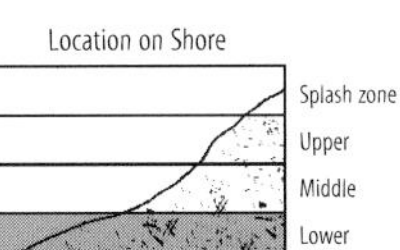

Habitat:	On rocky & gravelly shores & in shallow water
Colour:	Reddish-brown, green or yellow
Size:	Carapace up to 7cm across

Common Hermit Crab

Pagurus bernhardus
(Eupagurus bernhardus)

Faocha ghliomaigh

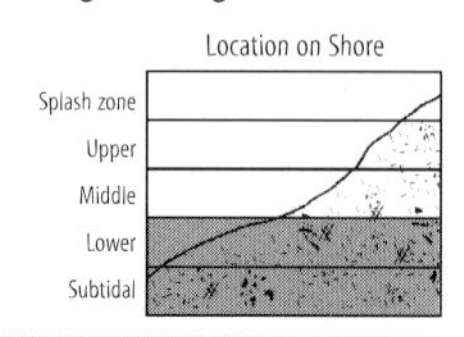

Habitat:	Often in rockpools or on sand or mud in shallow water
Colour:	Body reddish-brown
Size:	3-10cm

If you see a shell on legs moving quickly across the floor of a rockpool, what you may be seeing is a Common Hermit Crab. Unlike most, the hard **carapace** of this crab does not cover the whole body. To protect its soft **abdomen** it "borrows" an empty **mollusc** shell, moving to a larger one every time it grows. If disturbed, the hermit crab can retreat right into the shell and close the opening with its right **pincer**, which is much larger than the left. It will also grip the inside of the shell with two tiny back legs, gaining a good hold.

Broad-clawed Porcelain Crab

Porcellana platycheles

Portán poirceallâin clúmhach

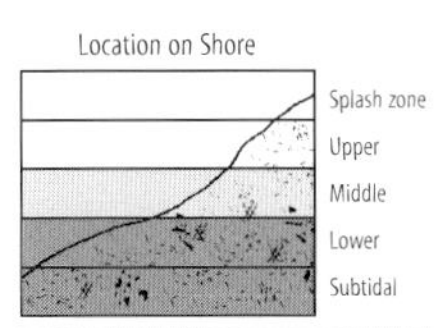

Habitat:	Under stones & in gravel on the rocky shore
Colour:	Dirty pale brown
Size:	Carapace up to 1.5cm across

Porcelain Crabs have very small, flat bodies and are usually found under rocks and stones. There are two different kinds of Porcelain Crab - the broad-clawed, which has wide, flat **pincers** and is covered with grey brown hair, and the long-clawed, which has long slender pincers and is not as hairy. In both, the **carapace** protecting the body is very round in outline, with no **rostrum** between the long **antennae** and eyes.

Scorpion Spider Crab

Inachus dorsettensis

Portán faoilinne scairpe

There are several species of spider crab to be found on the shore. All get their name from their long-legged, spidery appearance, although, unlike spiders, they have five pairs of walking legs, including the **pincers**. All spider crabs have a roughly triangular body. In the Scorpion Spider Crab, this may be heavily camouflaged with sponges and seaweed which it has picked off the rock and stuck to its shell. It has a curious habit of holding its pincers poised close to its body.

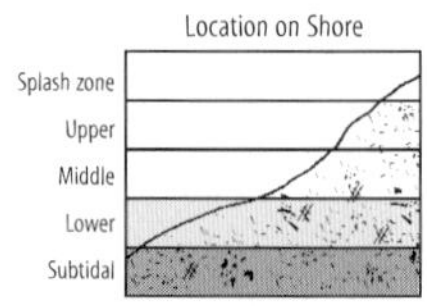

Habitat:	Among seaweed or under stones on rocky shores
Colour:	Yellow orange, sometimes disguised by sponges
Size:	Up to 15cm when legs extended

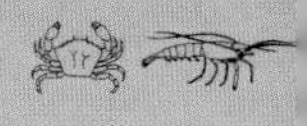

Squat Lobster

Galathea squamifera

Gliomach gogaideach

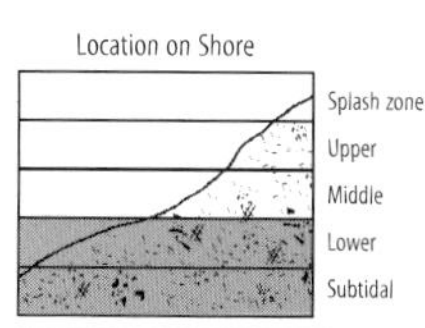

Habitat:	Under rocks & stones & in crevices
Colour:	Brown often with lighter & darker bands, often greenish
Size:	Carapace up to 3.5cm across but longer in length

The body of the Squat Lobster is oval-shaped and crab-like in appearance, but is flat for hiding in crevices. Brown-green in colour, it often has light and dark bands on its body. The first pair of walking legs is much longer than the rest and bears large **pincers**, while the last pair is very small. If disturbed, the Squat Lobster can jump backwards by flicking its **abdomen**, which is usually folded underneath the body. The stalked eyes and long **antennae** are separated by a triangular spike, or **rostrum**, which has a serrated edge.

Common Prawn

Palaemon serratus
(Leander serratus)

Cloicheán coiteann

The Common Prawn is transparent, unlike the shrimp (page 147), although it may have fluorescent yellow leg-joints and red and black lines on its body. Its body is narrow but not flattened and has a serrated spike, called the **rostrum**, projecting from the front of its head. On each side of the rostrum are the eyes and the long **antennae**. Unlike the shrimp, the first two pairs of walking legs have **pincers**. The prawn, which is often found in rockpools, can escape from **predators** by flicking its tail-like **abdomen**, causing it to shoot backwards.

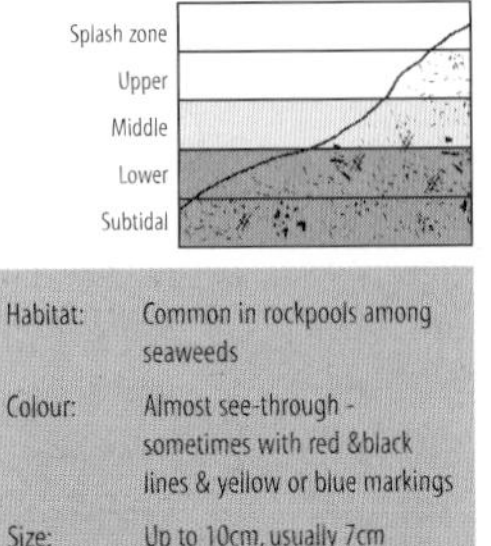

Habitat:	Common in rockpools among seaweeds
Colour:	Almost see-through - sometimes with red &black lines & yellow or blue markings
Size:	Up to 10cm, usually 7cm

Common Shrimp

Crangon crangon
(Crangon vulgaris)

Séacla

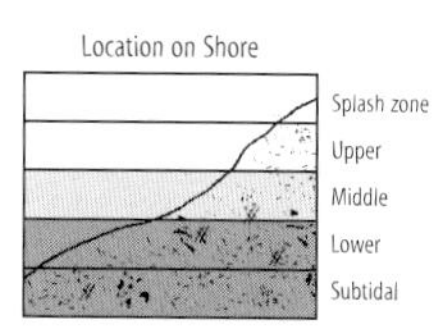

Habitat:	On sandy & muddy shores & in sandy rockpools
Colour:	Sandy, speckled with shades of brown
Size:	Up to 5cm

Closely related to prawns and lobsters, the Common Shrimp also has ten pairs of legs - five pairs of jointed walking legs at the front, and five pairs of flat, paddle-like swimming legs attached to its tail-like **abdomen**. The shrimp has a broad, flat body which is speckled and spotted in various shades of brown. This camouflage helps it blend with its surroundings. A pair of long **antennae** helps it feel for food and the first pair of walking legs has small **pincers** with which it feeds.

Sandhopper

Talitrus saltator

Dreancaid trá

Sandhoppers are found in large numbers on the beach. By day, they are found under seaweed and debris around the high tide mark; anywhere that provides a dark damp environment. At night, they come out to feed on seaweed. There are many different kinds of sandhopper. *Talitrus saltator* is a common species. The body is grey-brown and narrow, with the tail part slightly curled under. By flexing this tail, the Sandhopper can jump quite long distances.

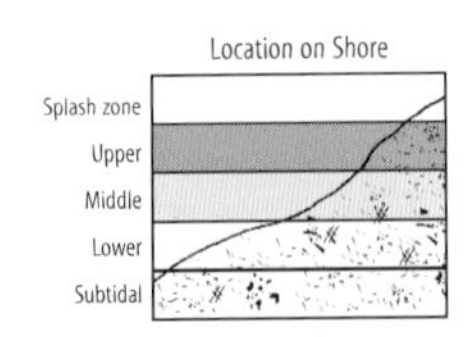

Habitat:	Under seaweed & debris on sandy beaches
Colour:	Grey-brown, yellow-brown
Size:	Up to 2cm

Common Sea Slater

Ligia oceanica

Cláirseach thrá

Location on Shore

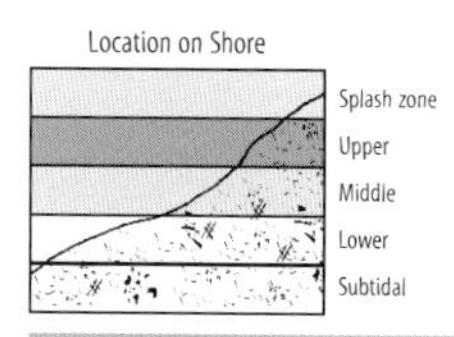

Habitat:	In crevices, under stones & under seaweeds
Colour:	Dark grey to brown
Size:	Up to 3cm

With its flat, jointed shape, this small **crustacean** looks like a woodlouse, and like a woodlouse it can roll into a ball if disturbed. It lives high on the upper shore and above the high tide mark in the splash zone, scavenging for food among the seaweed and debris of the **strandline**. During the day, it remains hidden under stones and in crevices, searching for food at night when there are fewer **predators** about.

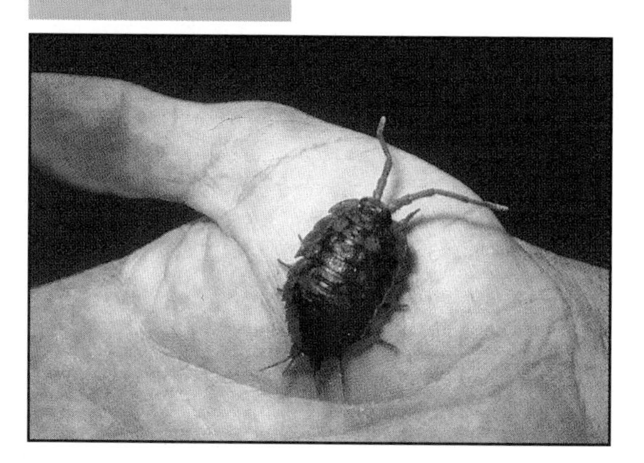

Common Acorn Barnacle

Semibalanus balanoides

Garbhán carraige coiteann

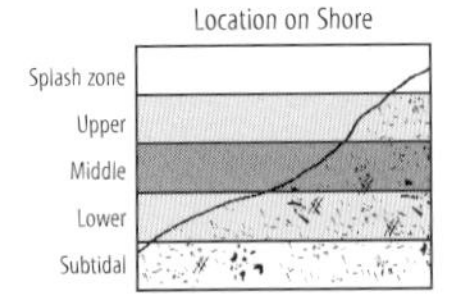

Habitat:	Cemented to rocks, stones & shells
Colour:	Greyish-white to yellowish
Size:	Up to 1.5cm

This tiny crustacean is very common, often covering large areas of a rocky shore. Its body is protected by a hard, cone-shaped shell which is made up of six **plates.** It is greyish-white to yellowish in colour and has an opening at the top of the cone. This opening is covered by four smaller plates. When the tide is in, these four plates open and feathery legs reach out to sieve food from the water. There are a few different types of barnacle, but because it is difficult to tell them apart, we mention only one species here.

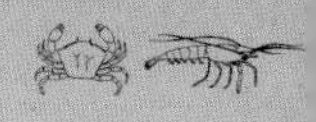

Goose Barnacle

Lepas anatifera

Giúrann

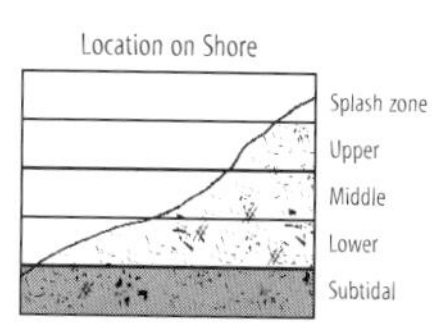

Habitat:	Stuck to any floating structures e.g. boats, driftwood
Colour:	White plates with bluish-grey tinge, with dark brown skin
Size:	5cm long

This is an unusual type of barnacle that is sometimes found washed up on the beach. It normally spends its life out at sea, attached to floating objects such as boats or driftwood. It holds on, using a long flexible brown stalk that can be partly withdrawn. This stalk is actually part of its head. The Goose Barnacle's shell is up to 5cm long and is made up of 5 white-to-bluish-grey **plates** set on dark brown skin. It feeds in the same way as other barnacles, by filtering tiny particles from the water.

Starfish & Sea Urchins

Starfish and sea urchins belong to a group of animals known as **echinoderms** - the spiny-skinned animals. As their name suggests, they all have spiny skins, although in some the spines are quite soft and not very obvious.

As well as spines, echinoderms also share another feature. They have bodies which are divided into equal sections, radiating out from a central point - a little like the spokes of a bicycle wheel. This is more obvious in starfish than in sea urchins. However, if you look at the empty shell of a sea urchin, you can see that it is divided into segments, rather like an orange.

A typical starfish

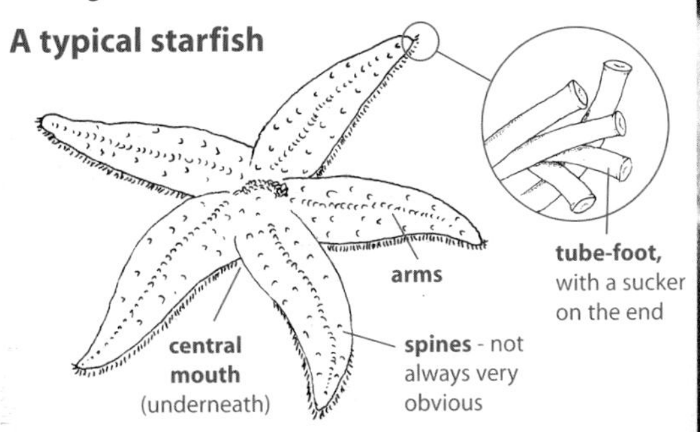

On most rocky shores, **starfish** are the commonest echinoderms found. Most have five **arms** (although some kinds have more) and these can be rough and spiny or quite smooth to the touch. On the underside of the arms, there are lots of small **tube-feet** with suckers on the end, which are used for moving the animal about and for feeding. The suckers on some are powerful enough to pull open **bivalves**. Once open, a starfish can stick its stomach out its mouth, which is underneath its body, and into the bivalve. It uses **digestive juices** to soften the animal and then absorbs it.

A typical brittlestar

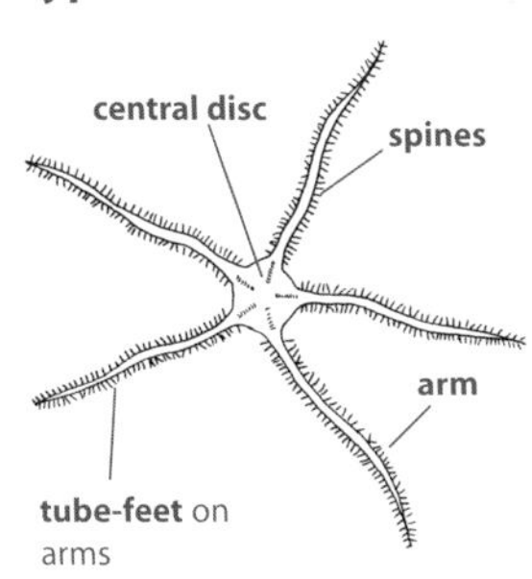

Closely related to starfish are the **brittlestars**. These spider-like starfish have long, thin arms. The arms, which are delicate and break quite easily, radiate out from a **central disc**. Brittlestars hide under rocks and stones when the tide goes out. Although they have tube-like feet, these are suckerless so they use their arms to pull themselves along - often very rapidly. Because of their small size, brittlestars feed on smaller animals or debris, waving their arms in the water, trapping tiny particles and carrying them to their mouth.

All brittlestars and starfish have an amazing ability to re-grow lost arms. Occasionally, starfish are found with only one long original arm and four smaller stubs that are re-growing. Such starfish are known as "comet forms".

Though not as common on the shore as the starfish, the **sea urchin** is quite easy to identify, with a rounded, spiny shell protecting a soft body inside. Unlike starfish, sea urchins are grazers, eating only **encrusting seaweeds**. The mouth of the sea urchin is on the underside of the body and contains five strong teeth which are used to scrape seaweed from the rocks. When living, the round shell contains the soft body of the sea urchin and it feels surprisingly heavy - though it is safer not to pick it up because of its sharp **spines**. If the sea urchin dies, these spines drop off and the body rots, leaving an empty shell. This shell is called a **test**.

A typical sea urchin

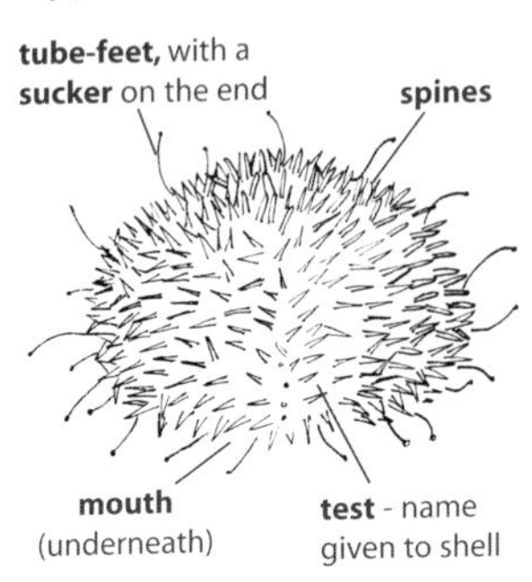

Like a starfish, the sea urchin also has tube-feet with suckers. These feet are long and are found all over its body, in between the spines. Usually seen only when the sea urchin is covered by water, they help it move about and also anchor the animal in one spot.

Common Starfish

Asterias rubens

Crosóg mhara choiteann

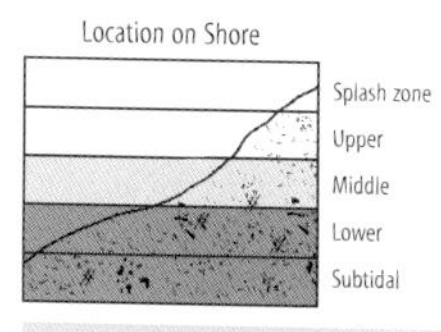

Habitat:	On rocky, sandy & gravel shores, among rocks & in rockpools
Colour:	Usually orange-brown or mauve above, but paler underneath
Size:	Up to 50cm across, but those on the shore are much smaller

This five-armed starfish has a very rough upper surface, with blunt **spines** that are embedded in its skin. The skin itself can vary in colour from orange to pale brown to mauve. Like many starfish, it has hundreds of tiny **tube-feet** underneath its arms, each ending in a sucker. These are used for movement and feeding. The tips of the **arms** are **light sensitive** and so are also used for finding food. Large starfish are uncommon on the shore, but small ones are often found among rocks and stones and in rockpools.

Cushion Star/ Starlet

Asterina gibbosa

Crosóg fhaoilinne

Looking like a small star-shaped pin-cushion, the Cushion Star is easily identified by its short stubby **arms**. It is one of the commonest **echinoderms** to be found on the lower shore, often on or under rocks and seaweed. However, its small size and green to pale-brown colouring make it difficult to find. Even though it rarely grows bigger than 3cm across, like larger starfish the Cushion Star feeds on worms, brittlestars and other small **encrusting animals**.

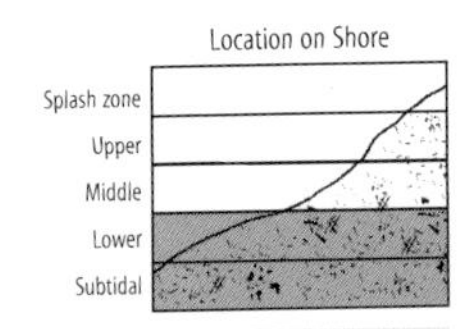

Habitat:	On & under rocks, stones & seaweeds on the rocky shore
Colour:	Green to pale brown
Size:	Up to 5cm across, but those on the shore are much smaller

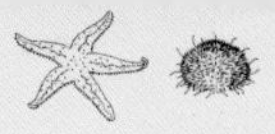

Spiny Starfish

Marthasterias glacialis

Crosóg choilgneach

Location on Shore

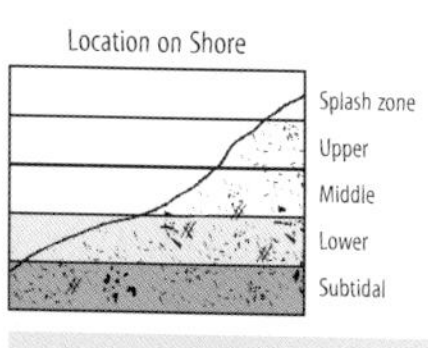

Habitat:	On rocky shores
Colour:	Blue-grey with purple tips to arms, creamy white underneath
Size:	Up to 80cm across, but those on the shore are much smaller

This is one of the largest starfish to be found on the seashore. It has five **arms** and many **tube-feet**. Its upper surface bears distinct **spines** which are surrounded by tiny pincer-like organs. These pincers are used to clear debris from the skin surface, which is usually a blueish-grey colour. The tips of its arms are often tinged with purple, and may be **light sensitive**. Spiny Starfish eat shellfish such as scallops and mussels, prising the shells open with their tube-feet.

Scarlet/Henry's Starfish

Henricia oculata

Crosóg Anraí

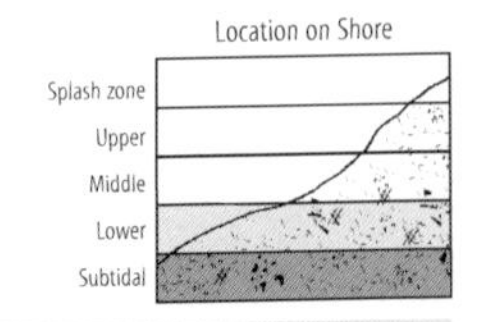

Habitat:	On rocky shores among small stones
Colour:	Blood-red to purple, creamy underneath
Size:	Up to 12cm across

This attractive, rock-dwelling starfish has bright blood-red or purple colouring, giving rise to its nickname of "bloody Henry". It has a rigid body and smooth, chalky skin that sometimes feels slimy because of a mucus coating. Its **tube-feet** can be pulled into a groove which runs the length of the undersides of its five arms. These feet are small and have no suckers. As well as feeding on small **invertebrates** such as sponges and **hydroids**, this starfish also feeds on tiny food particles that stick to the mucus covering its arms.

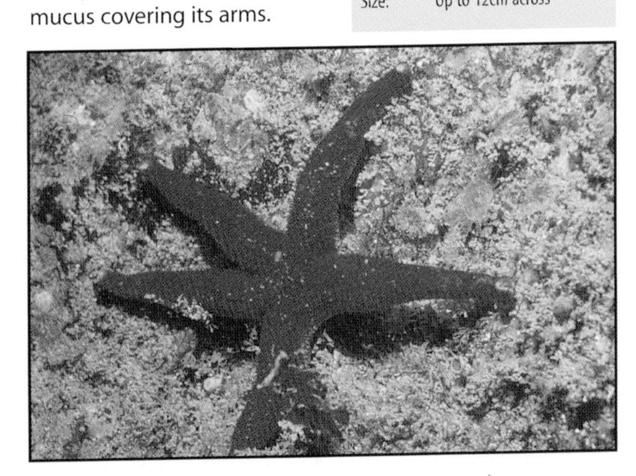

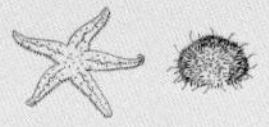

Sand Star

Astropecten irregularis

Crosóg ghainimh

Location on Shore

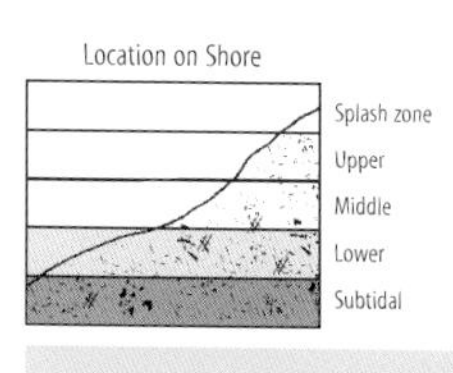

Habitat:	On sand & sandy gravel
Colour:	Orange-brown, paler underneath
Size:	Up to 12cm across

The Sand Star usually lives buried just below the surface of sand or gravel, a faint imprint being the only visible sign of its presence. Its upper surface is fairly smooth and orange brown in colour. The five **arms** are flat and are bordered by a fringe of pale cream **spines**. The **tube-feet**, which do not have suckers, are used for digging into the soft seabed. The Sand Star feeds on worms, small shrimp and other starfish and brittlestars.

Common Brittlestar

Ophiothrix fragilis

Crosóg bhriosc choiteann

As the name suggests, the Common Brittlestar is quite a fragile starfish and should be handled carefully, if at all. It has long, thin and very spiny **arms** and these are attached to a **central disc**, which also bears short spines. As in all brittle stars, the **tube-feet** do not have suckers; instead, the animal moves by pulling itself along with its arms. Common Brittlestars can be many different colours, with beautiful patterns on the top. They are usually found under stones and seaweeds, often in large groups, on the lower shore.

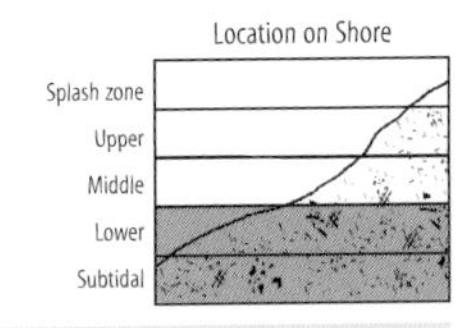

Habitat:	Under rocks, stones & seaweeds on the rocky shore
Colour:	Varies, red, brown, white, purple
Size:	Central disc up to 2cm across

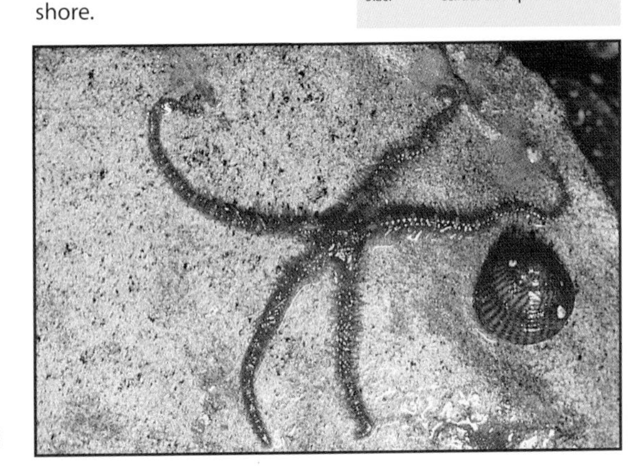

Black Brittlestar

Ophiocomina nigra

Crosóg bhriosc dhubh

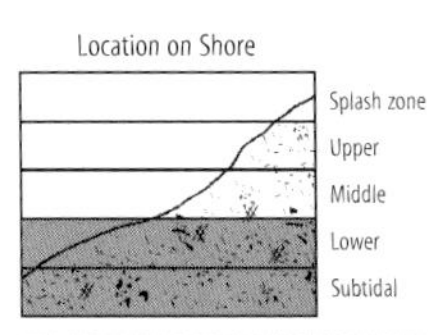

Habitat:	Under rocks & stones on the rocky shore
Colour:	Black-brownish-grey
Size:	Central disc up to 3cm across

The Black Brittlestar is very similar to the Common Brittlestar (page 160). However, there are some obvious differences. It has a rounder **central disc** which is smooth, and has fewer **spines** on its **arms**. It is usually black-brown in colour and is rarely patterned. The Black Brittlestar is often found with the Common Brittlestar in large groups, especially where there are strong tidal currents carrying food. Both feed by waving their arms in the water and trapping tiny particles on them. These are carried to the mouth by the **tube-feet**.

Sand Brittlestar

Ophiura ophiura
(Ophiura texturata)

Crosóg bhriosc ghainimh

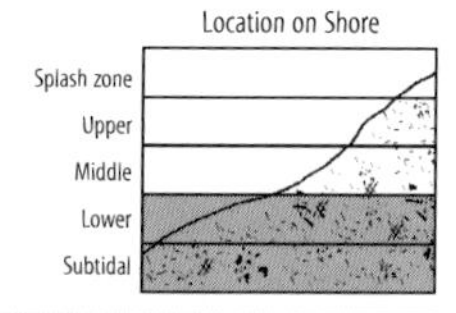

Habitat:	Buried in sand
Colour:	Orange-brown, paler brown underneath
Size:	Central disc up to 3cm across

This brittlestar is commonly found in sandy areas, where it remains buried just below the surface until feeding time. It is different from other commonly-found brittlestars in that it has shorter, stiffer **arms**. The **central disc** is fairly smooth but has a scale-like appearance. Its colouring, varying from orange brown to a pale sandy brown, is perfectly suited to help camouflage it in its environment.

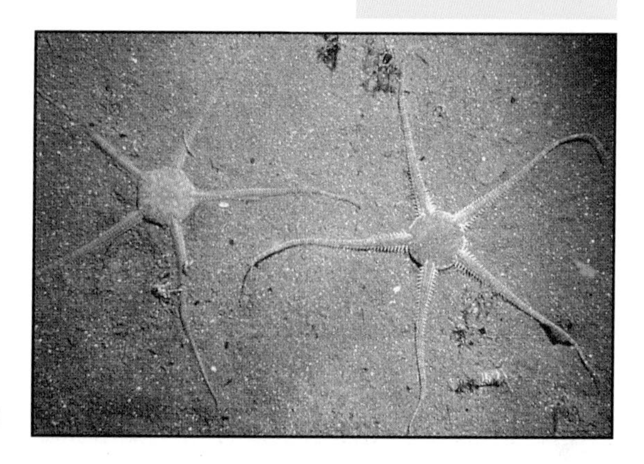

Featherstar

Antedon bifida

Cleiteach mhara

Location on Shore

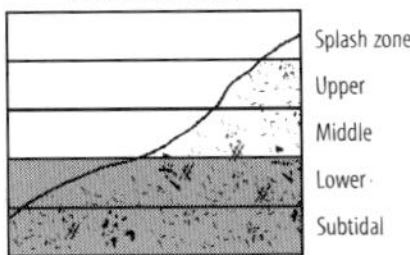

Habitat:	On rocky shores, in rockpools and attached to large seaweeds
Colour:	Red-brown, sometimes banded with white
Size:	5-15cm across

The Featherstar can sometimes be mistaken for a seaweed. It has delicate feathery **arms** that can measure up to 15cm across. These arms move slowly in the water, catching tiny food particles. Its root-like base enables it to hold on to rocks and to crawl. The Featherstar is usually reddish-brown in colour and may sometimes have white bands. It lives on rocks and in crevices on the lower shore and in shallow waters, where it is often found in large groups.

Edible Sea Urchin

Echinus esculentus

Cuán mara coiteann

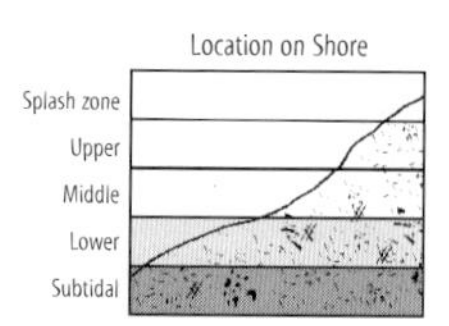

Habitat:	On rocks, boulders & kelp
Colour:	Red, pink, white with purple tips on spines
Size:	Up to 18cm across (including spines), usually smaller

The Edible Sea Urchin is the largest urchin to be found around Irish coasts. Empty shells, or **tests**, are commonly seen washed up on the shore. The shell is fairly thick and strong, offering good protection against **predators** and damage from waves. It is found in shades of pink, red and purple and has white spines, which often have purple or yellowish tips. It feeds on tiny seaweeds, and on any **encrusting animals** that it can scrape off the rocks.

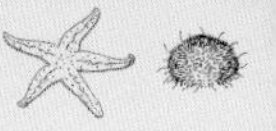

Black Sea Urchin/ Rock-boring Urchin

Paracentrotus lividus

Cuán mara dubh

Location on Shore

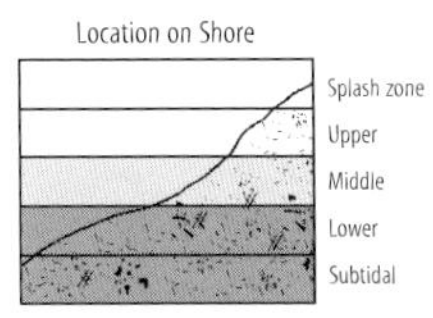

Habitat:	On the rocky shore, often in rockpools
Colour:	Green to dark brown to purple
Size:	Up to 12cm across (including spines)

The Black Sea Urchin is easily recognised by its dark colour, varying from dark green through brown to dark purple. It also has a habit of making shallow burrows or pits in the rock, in which to shelter. To do this, it moves its strong **spines** backwards and forwards to grind away at the rock. The Black Sea Urchin is often found in large numbers. Although it usually lives in warmer waters, it can be found as far north as the west coast of Ireland because of the warm sea currents of the Gulf Stream or North Atlantic Drift.

Green Sea Urchin

Psammechinus miliaris

Cuán mara glas

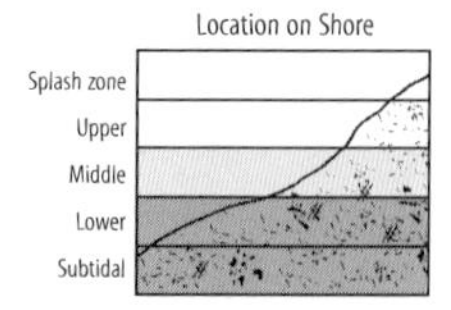

Habitat:	On rocky shores, often among kelp
Colour:	Green, with purple tips to spines
Size:	Up to 7cm, (including spines) usually smaller

This small sea urchin is common on the seashore but can be hard to find. It has a habit of covering itself with bits of gravel, shells or seaweed, which are held by its **tube-feet**. It can be found on the lower part of a rocky shore, particularly under boulders and among kelp **holdfasts** (page 46-47). The shell, or **test**, is slightly flat and is greenish in colour; the short **spines** are green with purple tips, and there is sometimes a whitish or pinkish tinge to the area around the mouth, which is underneath the urchin's body.

Sea Potato/ Heart Urchin

Echinocardium cordatum

Croídín buí

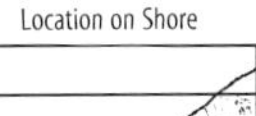
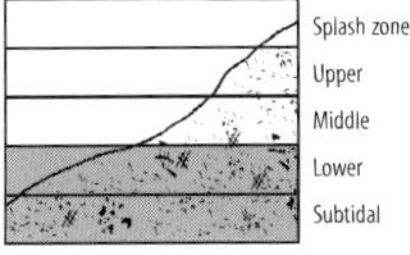

Habitat:	Buried in sand or found washed ashore
Colour:	Whitish test, yellowish-brown spines
Size:	Up to 9cm, usually smaller

The Sea Potato gets its common name from the potato-like appearance of its empty whitish **test**, which is sometimes found washed up on the shore. It usually lives in deeper waters where it can burrow into clean sand. Covered in a thick layer of yellowish-brown **spines** that point backwards, the Sea Potato can grow up to 9cm but is usually smaller. It is a **deposit feeder** and uses rows of **tube-feet** to collect particles from within its burrow.

Fish

When we think of **fish**, we usually imagine the large varieties that swim about freely in the sea. But on the seashore there are many small fish that have adapted to living in pools, under rocks and among damp seaweeds.

The seashore can be a very difficult and dangerous place to live. There are numerous **predators** on land, in the sea, and in the air, so many fish have protective camouflage, slippery skin or poisonous spines to help them avoid being eaten. But being eaten is not the only problem they have. Breathing can be difficult out of water, and there is always the possibility of drying out or of being battered by the waves.

Although some fish have made the shore their permanent home, other fish are trapped there by the tide. Often the young of fish living in the deeper water below the low tide will visit the shore to feed. Occasionally, the incoming tide will wash them onto the rocks or they are stranded in rockpools when the tide goes out. Young flatfish (page 183) are sometimes trapped in this way.

Fish are vertebrates, which means that they have a backbone. Most fish also have an swim bladder inside their body which helps to keep them afloat.

Fish breathe by taking in oxygen from the water. As water flows over the **gills**, which are on each side of the head, oxygen is taken in and passed to the blood.

Although most fish can survive only when totally covered by water, some fish, such as the shanny/blenny (page 171), have adapted well to the ever-changing conditions on the seashore. When the tide goes out, these fish will survive in the wet areas under seaweeds and rocks until the tide comes in again.

Fish have fins, which vary in shape and number in different species (see below).

A typical fish

tail fin

some have an obvious line called the **lateral line**

dorsal fins - may have one or more

gills - used for breathing

eyes

mouth

anal fin - may have one or more

most have **scales** covering the body

pectoral fin (1 of a pair)

pelvic fin (1 of a pair)

Some fins have developed to suit particular situations. Fins can be either paired (one on each side of the body) or unpaired (usually running along the back or belly). The **tail fin** is the fin that is usually used to propel the fish through the water, though the **pectoral fins** are sometimes used for this, as well as for steering.

Fish are usually covered with **scales**, though some have more of an armour-like covering. The scales provide protection from predators. The markings, often colourful, help camouflage the fish from enemies, by making them very hard to see. Some markings frighten enemies, and others help fish to identify each other.

When trying to spot fish in a rockpool, it is important to sit quietly and to be still. It is always best to sit with the rockpool between you and the sun, so that you won't cast a shadow over it and frighten the fish. Sunglasses may help to reduce the reflection from the surface of the water.

When trying to identify fish there are a number of things that are important to note: the shape and colour of the body and any markings on the skin, for example a **lateral line** (this is full of nerves to "sense" movement near the fish); the number and shape of the fins; and whether or not there are spines or **barbels** in the head area. Barbels are soft, beard-like feelers that help some fish find food, which for many fish is **plankton** or small surrounding animals. Knowing the signs to look for will help you identify some of the fish you will find. Remember, however, that a fish may be from deeper water and simply stranded in the rockpool until the tide comes in again. It may be necessary to look in other books to identify it.

Shanny/Blenny

Lipophrys pholis
(Blennius pholis)

Ceannruán

Location on Shore

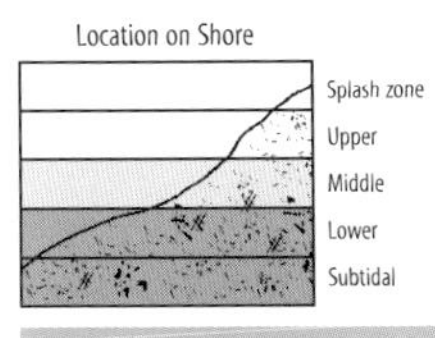

Habitat:	In rockpools & among seaweed on rocky shores
Colour:	Mottled green & olive
Size:	Up to 16cm

Its wide lips and habit of supporting itself on its leg-like **pectoral fins**, give the Shanny a clown-like appearance. Its mottled green and olive colouring provides the perfect camouflage for living under seaweeds and rocks on the lower shore and in shallow waters. It has a single **dorsal fin** which extends almost to the **tail fin**, and a tough, scaleless skin which is covered in mucus to reduce water loss. This commonly-found shore fish feeds on worms, shrimp and other **crustaceans** such as barnacles and small crabs.

Sand Goby

Pomatoschistus minutus

Mac siobháin gainimh

As in many shore fish, the eyes of the Sand Goby are on top of its head. This allows it to lie hidden, partly buried in the sand at the bottom of a rockpool, with just its eyes showing. Its body, which is sandy-beige in colour, with darker and lighter speckles and a silvery sheen, is perfectly camouflaged against the sand bottom of a rockpool. Sand Gobies have two separate **dorsal fins**. In the male Sand Goby, the back edge of the first dorsal fin bears a dark blue/black spot.

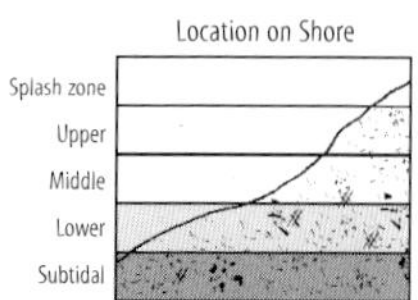

Habitat:	In sandy rockpools & shallow waters
Colour:	Sandy beige, pale speckled brown, with darker banding
Size:	Up to 10 cm

Rock Goby

Gobius paganellus

Mac siobháin carraige

The Rock Goby, as its name suggests, is commonly found on rocky shores where its dark, mottled body provides good camouflage against a background of rocks and seaweed. As in all gobies, its **pelvic fins** form a fan-shaped sucker which helps prevent the fish being washed away by the waves. All Rock Gobies have a contrasting band of yellow, orange, or pale brown along the top of their first **dorsal fin**. This helps to tell them apart from other species.

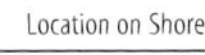

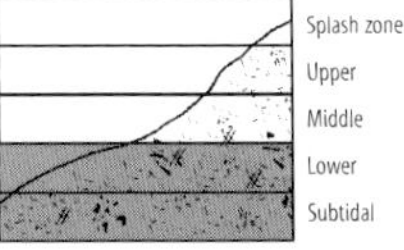

Habitat:	On the rocky shore among seaweeds & in rockpools
Colour:	Varies - usually dark mottled brown with an orange or lighter band on front dorsal fin
Size:	Up to 12cm

Two-spotted Goby

Gobiusculus flavescens

Mac siobháin buí

Although it's called the Two-spotted Goby, only the female has two spots - a single one on each side, at the base of the tail. The male, in addition to these spots, also has one behind each **pectoral fin**, making a total of four. The two-spotted goby is smaller and more delicate than other gobies, having a slender body. It also differs in its behaviour, preferring to swim in small **shoals** among the seaweed, in shallow water and rockpools.

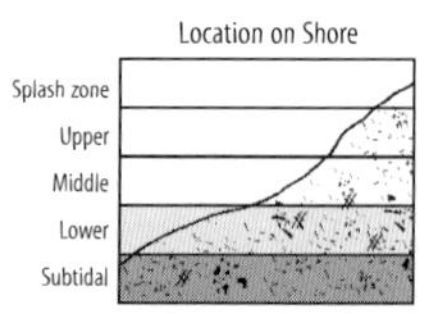

Habitat:	Among seaweed in rockpools & shallow water
Colour:	Mottled reddish-brown with darker spots
Size:	Up to 6cm

Butterfish/ Gunnel

Pholis gunnellus

Sleamhnóg

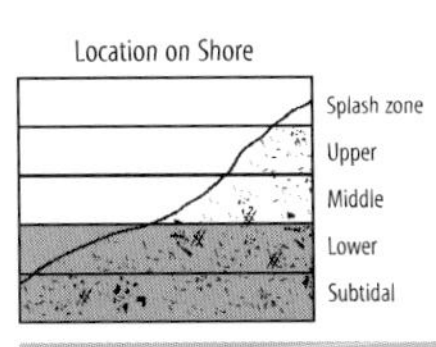

Habitat:	In pools & under stones on rocky shores
Colour:	Mottled brown with dark spots along dorsal fin & paler underside
Size:	Up to 20cm

Long and eel-like with a slimy, slippery skin, the Butterfish is often found under rocks and stones. It is usually brown in colour with pale, whitish-brown shading on the belly. Along its back there are dark spots on each side of its long **dorsal fin**. The slimy mucus on its body helps make it difficult for a **predator** to get a good grip on the fish and also helps reduce water loss from the body. Butterfish, noted for their sad facial expression, are one of the most common fish on the shore. They feed on small shrimp, worms and anything else of a suitable size.

Greater Pipefish

Syngnathus acus

Snáthaid mhara mhór

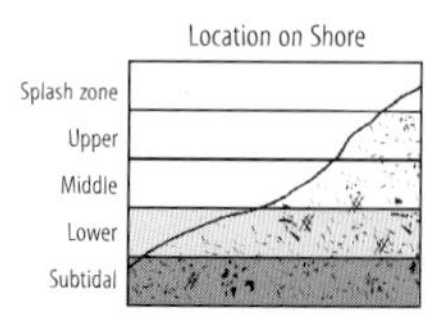

Habitat:	In rockpools & among seaweeds & rocks
Colour:	Dark brown above with paler cream belly
Size:	Up to 15cm

Several kinds of pipefish are found around our coasts. In all, the body is covered by hard, bony plates, like a suit of armour, giving it a rigid feel. Like their relatives, the seahorses, pipefish have long, thin bodies and can swim in an upright position. With a dark and often patchy colouring, they are well camouflaged for hiding among **fronds** of seaweed and in rockpools. Pipefish feed by sucking in the tiny animals and plants in seawater, called **plankton**, through their tube-like mouths.

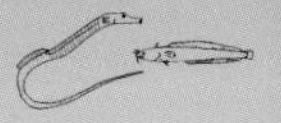

Five-bearded Rockling

Ciliata mustela

Donnán cúig ribe

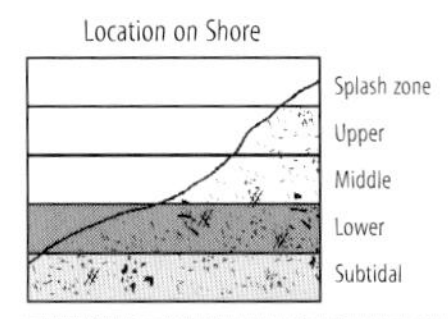

Habitat:	In rockpools & under rocks & stones on rocky shores
Colour:	Brown above, silvery-white below
Size:	Up to 20cm

The five sensitive **barbels** around the mouth give this fish its name, and help it to find the small animals on which it feeds. Its body is long and has slippery skin, allowing it to slide among rocks and stones. Its rich brown colouring and silvery-white belly camouflage it among the sand, mud and brown seaweeds. Its small first **dorsal fin**, which lies in a groove on the back, is another identifying feature. The related Three-bearded Rockling (see inset) differs in having only three barbels and a paler body.

Father Lasher/ Short-spined Sea Scorpion

Myxocephalus scorpius

Scairpiasc spíonghearr

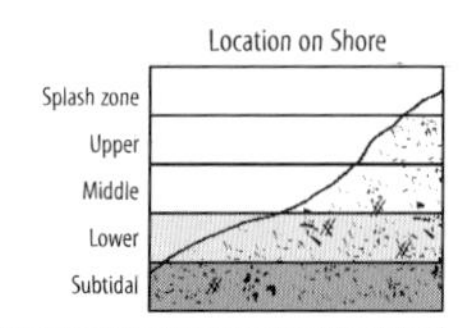

Habitat:	Among seaweeds in shallow waters
Colour:	Varies - mottled green, grey, reddish-brown
Size:	Up to 30cm

This fish gets one of its common names from the spines on its mouth, head and **gill covers**. It has a head that appears bigger than the rest of its body and a large mouth which it uses for feeding on shrimp and small fish. Its skin, which is mottled green, grey and brown on top, and paler underneath, is well camouflaged in seaweeds and shallow waters. The markings can sometimes change to suit the background.

Fifteen-spined/ Sea Stickleback

Spinachia spinachia

Garmachán farraige

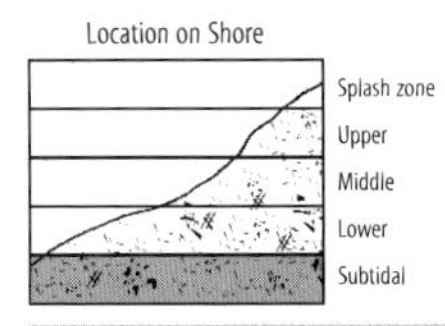

Habitat:	Among seaweed and rocks in rockpools & shallow waters
Colour:	Olive brown back with silvery belly
Size:	Up to 20cm, but usually smaller

This fish has about fifteen small spines on its back, in front of its **dorsal fin**, giving it its name. Olive brown in colour, with a silvery belly, its long slender body is held fairly rigid. Its mouth is small and delicate and is used to pick small shrimp from crevices, as well as for snipping the legs off barnacles for food. This fish is found in pools on the lower shore and in shallow water, where it hovers among rocks and seaweed.

Shore Clingfish/ Cornish Sucker

Lepadogaster lepadogaster

Súmaire Cornach

This fish gets its name from its habit of clinging to rocks and seaweed with its **pelvic fins**, which act like a sucker on its belly. The body is slightly slimy and has a rubbery, scaleless skin. Its smooth, streamlined shape, flat below and rounded on top, combined with its sucker, help it to live in lower shores where the waves can be very strong. The colour can vary a lot but markings on the back of the head, which often include two blue spots, can resemble a pair of eyes and glasses.

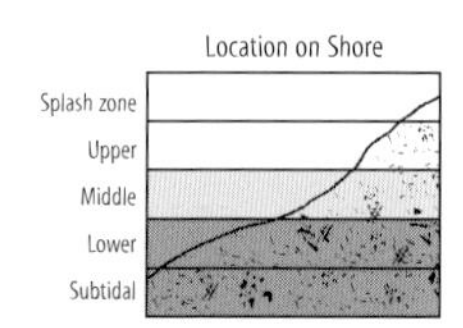

Habitat:	Among rocks & in pools & shallow waters
Colour:	Reddish-brown with two blue spots behind the eyes
Size:	Up to 7cm

Lesser Weever Fish

Echiichthys vipera
(Trachinus vipera)

Goineadóir

Location on Shore

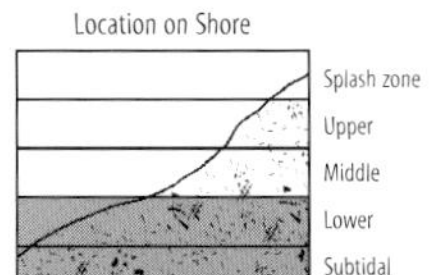

Habitat:	Clean sandy shores
Colour:	Mottled yellow-brown above, whitish below
Size:	Up to 15cm

With just its eyes showing, the Lesser Weever fish buries itself in the sand on the lower shore and in shallow water. Its **gill covers** and **dorsal fin** have poisonous spines which it uses as a defence against being eaten by larger fish. These spines can also inflict a painful sting if stood on. The Lesser Weever fish can be recognised by its upwardly-tilted mouth and eyes. Its back is a mottled yellow-brown, while its belly is paler. Lesser Weever fish will feed on anything of a suitable size, including shrimp, crabs and fish.

Lesser Sand Eel

Ammodytes tobianus

Corr ghainimh bheag

Sand Eels are not found in rockpools, but may often be seen swimming by the edge of the shore in large **shoals**. They can grow to 20cm in length and have long, slender bodies with pointed heads and a lower jaw longer than the upper. They are covered in small, silvery **scales** that seem to shine in the water as they swim. They live in sandy areas in shallow water, and spend much of their time buried in the sand or in shingle.

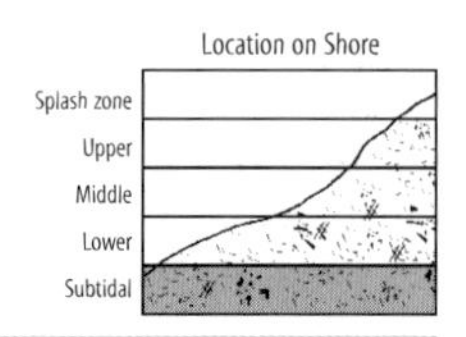

Habitat:	In shallow waters & offshore
Colour:	Green on back, silvery white below
Size:	Up to 20cm

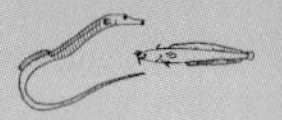

Flatfish

Leathóg

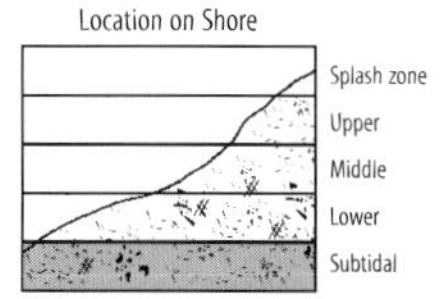

Habitat:	In shallow to deep waters
Colour:	Speckled sandy brown
Size:	2-8cm common in rockpools, up to 40cm when adult

Shallow waters and sandy-bottomed rockpools are often hiding places for young flatfish. Each fish lies on its side; the underside is usually white, while the top is a speckled brown to match the seabed. Flatfish bury themselves in the sand with only their eyes showing, so that they are camouflaged from any **predators**. There they lie in wait for food such as sandhoppers and shrimp. Plaice, Flounder and Dab are some flatfish that may be seen by the shore. Plaice are the most easily identified, as they have reddish-orange spots.

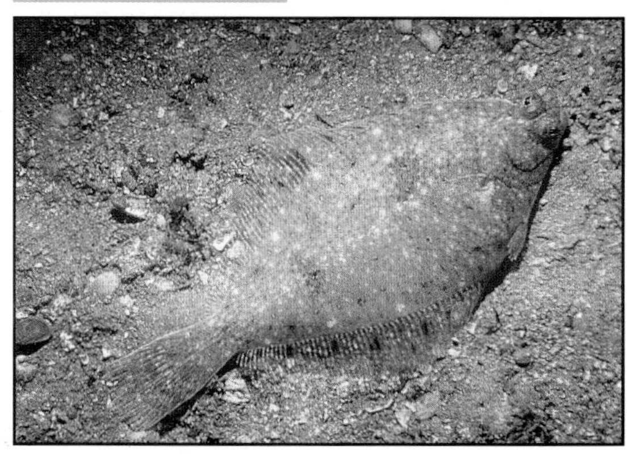

Bits & Bobs

If you walk on the shore, along the **high tide** mark, you will often find debris that has been left behind by the outgoing tide. Sometimes, unusual objects are found on this **strandline**. These may be animals and plants that have been drifting in the sea, having been washed off the rocks. They may also have come from deeper waters, either floating freely or attached to wreckage.

Much of what is found is possibly dead. Due to the pounding of the waves, it is usual to find only small pieces of plants or animals. It is important to remember this when you are trying to identify them, as they can look very different when whole.

It is not possible to list everything that could be washed up. The ocean covers a huge area, and is inhabited by countless animals and plants. The following is just a sample of what can be seen.

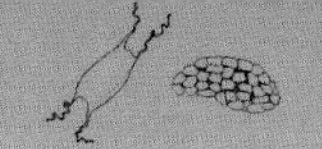

Mermaid's Purse

Scyliorhinus canicula

Sparán na caillí mairbhe

Location on Shore

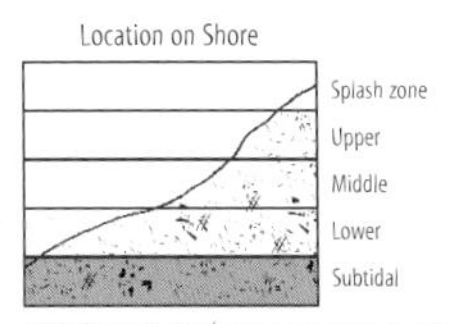

Habitat:	Offshore, but empty case often washed up
Colour:	Light to dark brown
Size:	Case up to 6cm long

The Mermaid's Purse is the egg case laid by the dogfish in deeper waters. It has long, twisted **tendrils** on each corner which are used to attach the egg case to seaweed and other floating structures. It is light brown and almost see-through. The egg case is usually only seen when it is washed up on the shore, and then it is often dry and hard. It is normally empty, as the young fish will have hatched by the time the case is washed ashore.

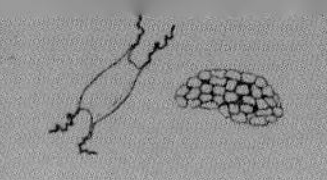

Common Cuttlefish (skeleton)

Sepia officinalis

Cudal (Cnámh)

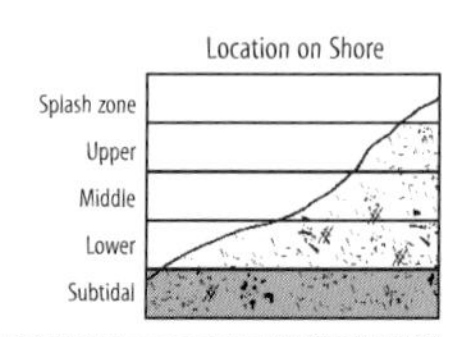

Habitat:	Cuttlefish lives offshore, but cuttlebone often washed up
Colour:	Cuttlebone - white
Size:	Up to 18cm

The Cuttlefish (see inset) belongs to the same family as the Octopus and Squid and lives in bays and **estuaries**. When the Cuttlefish is alive, the bone inside its body has many tiny holes which fill with gas. These helps it float. When the Cuttlefish dies and decays, the bone floats about in the water for a long time and is sometimes washed up on the shore. These bones are often given to pet budgerigars to help them keep their beaks trim.

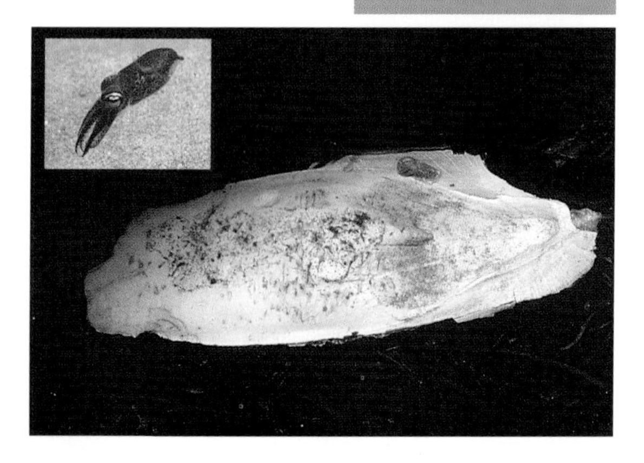

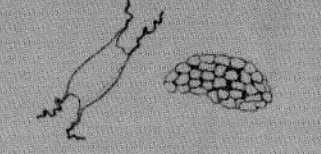

Common Whelk (eggmass)

Buccinum undatum (ova)

Cuachma (eochraí)

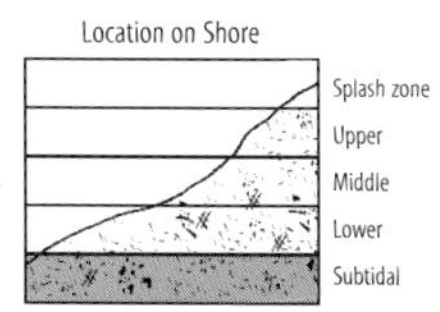

Habitat:	Common Whelk lives in shallow to deep waters; empty egg-mass often washed ashore
Colour:	Creamy yellow
Size:	Up to 8cm across

The eggs of the Common Whelk look like a mass of bubbles stuck together, each "bubble" containing one egg. When the eggs are freshly laid, they are spongy but they are rarely seen in that state. Usually, the egg-masses are empty by the time they have been washed up on the shore, as the young will already have hatched. The egg cases dry out on the beach and become very brittle. The animal that lays these eggs, the Common Whelk (see inset), is a **gastropod** that lives in deeper waters.

Hornwrack

Flustra foliacea

Teanga chait

Hornwrack looks like a plant, but in fact it is made up of many animals living together in a group, or **colony**. It is found in deep waters, and is only seen on the seashore when it is washed up after storms. In deeper waters, it can be found growing in huge beds on rocks and stones where it also provides food and shelter for a large variety of creatures. Its colour can range from cream, brown and green to yellow-grey.

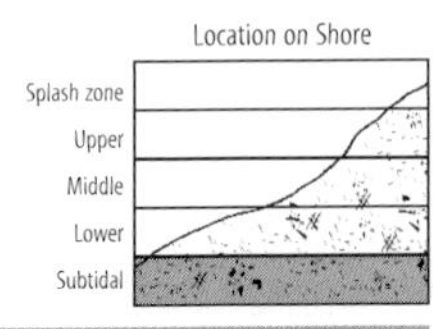

Habitat:	In shallow to deep waters on sandy ground
Colour:	Cream, brown, green to yellow-grey
Size:	Frond up to 6cm long

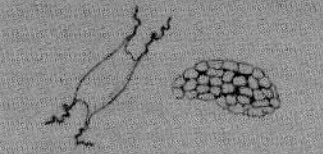

Sea Lemon (eggs)

Archidoris pseudoargus (ova)

Bodalach buí (eochraí)

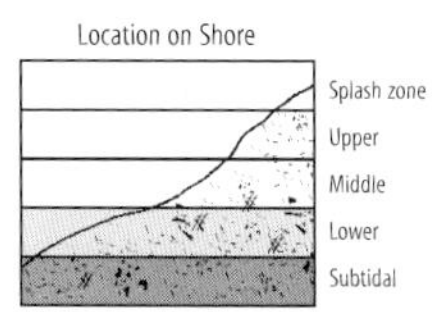

Habitat:	Sea Lemon lives in shallow waters, but moves up shore to lay eggs
Colour:	Sea Lemon creamy-yellow; Eggs creamy-white
Size:	Both several centimetres long

The eggs of the Sea Lemon are often found on the rocky shore, laid in a long, jelly-like coil. This coil can be up to several centimetres in length and is usually white or yellow in colour. The Sea lemon (seen below laying its eggs) is a **mollusc** and looks like a large slug. It is yellow in colour, with brown markings, and has a large **foot** and two **tentacles** on its head. At the other end of its body are its **gills**, which look like feathers. The Sea Lemon is usually found in shallow waters but it moves up the shore to lay its eggs.

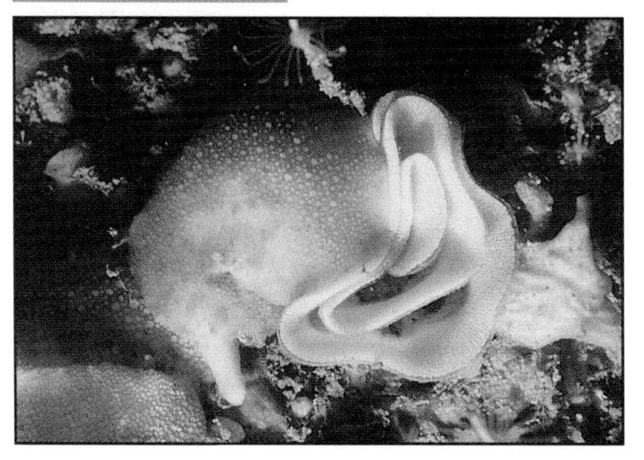

Glossary

Note: Drawings showing the structure of the various plants or animals mentioned in this book can be found in the introduction of each chapter. Some of the following words may be illustrated there.

abdomen: The part of an animal's body that contains many of the internal organs, including the stomach. It can vary in shape, for example in the prawn it looks like a tail.

air bladders: Air-filled sacs found in certain types of seaweeds and that help them float.

algae: Simple plants, made up of one or more cells, that grow mainly in water and lack true stems, roots and leaves, but usually contain chlorophyll (the green "colour" in plants). It is also the name given to a group of marine plants known as seaweeds. (The singular of algae is **alga**.)

antennae: Thin, delicate, often long stalks found on the heads of some marine animals. Can be used to smell, to hear and/or to pick up vibrations, and to sense heat.

arm: One of the main "limbs" of the starfish.

barbel: A short, flexible structure made of fleshy tissue that is found near the mouth of some fish and which is used for tasting and touching.

basal disc: The disc at the end of the **column**, which the sea anemone uses to attach itself to rocks.

bivalve: A **mollusc**, such as a mussel or an oyster, that has two shells joined together by a hinge-like **ligament**.

brackish water: A type of water found in most **estuaries.** This water contains less salt than the sea but, usually, more salt than freshwater.

bristle worm: A **free-living** worm that has hair-like bristles covering its body.

brown seaweed: One of the three main groups of seaweed, the others being **green** and **red**.

byssus threads: Threads that are produced by some **bivalves**, enabling them to attach themselves firmly to rocks and other structures.

calcareous: Made of chalk or calcium carbonate.

carapace: The main shell-like body of a **crustacean**.

cast: A spaghetti-like coil of sand/mud left behind on the shore by a worm.

central disc: The centre of the brittlestar, from which the **arms** grow.

classification: The system whereby animals, and plants, with similar characteristics are grouped. The largest group is called the kingdom. All animals belong in one kingdom and all plants belong in another. A kingdom is then divided into smaller groups, each of which is known as a phylum. For example, all animals with backbones (vertebrates) are put into one phylum. Each phylum is then divided again and again, each smaller group becoming more specific. These groups are: class, order, family, genus and species. One example of the genus and species name is *Carcinus* (genus) *maenas* (species), the Common Shore Crab.

claws: The tips of **crustaceans**' legs; used for gripping. Also known as **pincers**.

cnidarians: The name given to the group of jelly-like animals that includes sea anemones and jellyfish. This group was formally known as coelenterates.

colony: A group of individuals of the same type that live together.

column: The main body of the sea anemone, from which the **tentacles** grow.

crustacean: An animal that has no bones, but has a hard skeleton on the outside and many jointed legs.

decapod: A **crustacean** that has five pairs of walking legs. Decapod means "ten legs".

deposit feeding: A type of feeding whereby the animal takes in a mixture of water and sand/mud, extracts the food and then passes out the undigested material.

digestive juices: The juices in the stomach that break down food, making it easier to absorb into the body.

dorsal blood vessel: A large vein near the upper surface of the body and which contains blood.

dorsal fin: A **fin** found on the back or upper side of a fish.

echinoderms: A group of marine animals that includes starfish and sea urchins.

encrusting animals: Animals that grow flat and close to the rock. They include sponges, star ascidians and hydroids.

encrusting seaweeds: Plants that grow flat and close to the rock.

errant: An animal that moves about freely and is not attached to any structure.

estuary: The mouth of a river, where freshwater from the river meets the sea. Estuaries are affected by the tide.

exhalent opening: The opening in an animal which is used for breathing and for passing waste out of the body.

exhalent siphon: A tube, or opening, through which waste water is pumped out of an animal during feeding and breathing.

exposed shore: A shore that is subjected to strong wave action and which is not sheltered.

filter feeding: A method of feeding used by some marine animals. Small particles of food are sieved or filtered out of the water. Different methods of filter feeding are used by different animals.

fin: Part of a fish that helps it move, steer and balance.

flatworm: A worm that has a flat, leaf-like body, with **tentacles** and tiny eyes at the front.

foot: Found on the underside of the body of some animals, it is used for attaching to rocks and/or moving along the shore.

free-living: An animal or plant which lives unattached to any structure.

frond: The leaf-like part of a seaweed.

fungus: A plant-like **organism**, which does not produce chlorophyll (the green "colour" in plants) and which cannot produce its own food. Examples are yeast, mould and mushrooms.

gastropod: A group of **molluscs** that includes land and sea snails and which have a single, usually coiled, shell.

gill cover: The piece of skin covering a **gill**.

gills: Parts of the body, in most underwater animals, that are used for breathing. As water flows over them, oxygen is taken out and passed to the blood.

green seaweed: One of the three main groups of seaweed, the others being **brown** and **red**.

habitat: The natural home of a plant or animal.

herbivore: An animal that eats plants only.

high tide: The point at which the sea reaches its highest level, causing the land furthest up the shore to be covered by water.

holdfast: Usually a tough sticky pad used to attach a seaweed to rocks or solid structures.

hydroid: A type of animal that lives in a group, or **colony**, often forming a branching structure of **polyps** which attaches to seaweeds and rocks.

inhalent opening: The opening in an animal which it uses to draw water into its body, in order to breathe and feed.

inhalent siphon: A tube, or opening, which an animal uses to draw water into its body, in order to feed and breathe.

inter-tidal zone: The area between the **high** and **low tide** mark that is covered and uncovered by the tide twice a day.

invertebrates: All creatures that do not have a backbone, e.g. sponges, jellyfish, sea anemones, snails, worms and **crustaceans**.

iridescence: An oily or brilliant shine seen on some seaweeds and animals when underwater.

lateral line: A line that usually runs along the centre of a fish, from its **gills** to its tail. It is full of nerves to "sense" movement around the fish.

ligament: A band of strong tissue that connects bones and shells.

light sensitive: An animal or plant which reacts to light. In some, the eyes are light-sensitive: they cannot see clearly, but can tell the difference between light and dark and can also see movement.

low tide: The point at which the sea reaches its lowest level, leaving the shore exposed to the air.

lower shore: The lowest part of the shore uncovered by the tide.

marine: Of, from or affected by the sea.

middle shore: The area of the shore, between the highest and lowest levels.

midrib: A vein sometimes seen along the middle of the **frond** of a seaweed, rather like that on a leaf of a tree.

mollusc: An animal that usually has a soft body which is protected by a shell, although some molluscs do not have a shell. A mollusc is an **invertebrate.**

mouth arm: The mouth of a jellyfish, which is at the end of a tube that hangs down from the stomach, and which is often surrounded by tentacles.

mouth disc: The top opening of a sea anemone that

surrounds the mouth and which is visible when its **tentacles** are pulled in.

neap tide: A tide which has the smallest difference in water level between **high** and **low tide**.

operculum: A horny disc that covers the opening in some **gastropods**, when the foot is pulled in, to prevent the animal inside from drying out.

organism: Anything that is living.

parapodia: A pair of often paddle-like structures, used for movement in worms. In some worms they are also used for breathing. There are often many parapodia on each worm.

pectoral fin: A pair of **fins** found on the side of most fish.

pelvic fin: A pair of **fins** found on the underside of a fish's body.

photosynthesis: The process by means of which plants make food from sunlight and water. Photosynthesis takes place in the green part of plants, where chlorophyll (a substance which gives plants their green colour) absorbs energy from light.

pincer: The **claws** found on the legs of many **crustaceans** and which are used for gripping their prey.

plankton: Tiny animals and plants found floating in water. They are more easily seen using a microscope and are often the young (larvae) of marine animals.

plates: Shells that cover the body of a barnacle.

polyp: A **marine** animal that usually consists of a sac-like body with **tentacles** surrounding its mouth. Polyps can join together to form a **colony**, as in corals, or can be single, as in the sea anemone and the jellyfish.

predator: An animal that hunts and feeds on other animals.

rasping: A feeding method used by many **marine** grazers, such as limpets, where they use sharp teeth to scrape seaweeds off the rocks.

red seaweed: One of the three main groups of seaweed, the others being **green** and **brown**.

reproductive bodies/organs: Parts of plants/animals that are involved in producing new individuals.

rostrum: A point that forms on the outer skeleton of a **crustacean** to protect the head.

scales: Small and very thin plates on the skin of a fish.

scavengers: Animals who do not kill their own food but who feed on the bodies of dead animals.

scientific names: To avoid confusion, all plants and animals that have been identified have been given a scientific name. The language used for these names is Latin. Everyone around the world uses the same name for a given plant or animal, based on the system of **classification**. Normally there are two parts to the species name e.g. *Laminaria saccharina* (Sugar Kelp), the first part identifying a group and the second the particular plant within that group. Sometimes, the term *Laminaria* spp. is used when referring to all types of *Laminaria* (kelp) species. It is possible, over time, that the scientific name for an animal or plant might be changed. For some species in this book we have included the older name in (brackets). Latin is nearly always written in *italics*.

sedentary: Permanently attached to a surface and not **free-living**.

sheltered shore: A shore that is less subject to strong wave action than an **exposed shore**.

shoal: A large group of fish swimming together.

siphon: One or more tubes found in the bodies of **invertebrates**, and which are used for taking water in and out of the body.

solitary: Existing or living alone; without others.

spines: Sharp structures that generally stick out from the body of an animal and which are used for protection.

splash zone: The area on a shore that is not covered by the tide at any time, but which is often made wet by the salty spray of crashing waves.

spore: A small **reproductive body** that can grow into a new plant.

spring tide: A tide which has the largest difference in water level between **high** and **low tide**.

stipe: The stem of a seaweed.

strandline: Area along the **high tide** mark on a beach, where seaweed and debris often collect.

subtidal zone: The area of the shore that is always covered by water and is found below the **low tide** mark.

tail fin: The **fin** at the tail-end of a fish.

tendril: A long, thin, coiling extension, used by an animal or plant to attach itself to a structure.

tentacles: Long, flexible extensions used by some animals for grabbing, holding or feeling.

test: The shell which covers the body of the sea urchin. It is covered with spines when the animal is alive, but these fall off when the animal dies.

thallus: The main body of a lichen, which has no stem, roots or leaves.

thorax: The middle section of the body of an **invertebrate** which usually bears the legs.

tooth: A pointed ridge near the opening of a shell.

tube-feet: Muscular tubes, often with suckers on the ends, that help starfish and sea urchins to move and feed.

upper shore: The highest part of the shore covered by the incoming tide.

valve: One of a pair of shells, found in **bivalve molluscs**.

zonation: The positioning of animals and plants on the shore, relative to the level of the tide.

Further Reading

Hamlyn Guide to **Seashores and Shallow Seas of Britain and Europe**. Andrew Campbell. ISBN 0-600-58376-7

Collins Pocket Guide **Seashore of Britain & Europe**. Peter Hayward, Tony Helson-Smith, Chris Shields. ISBN 0-00-219955-6

Sherkin Island Marine Station's **Ireland's Marine Life. A World of Beauty**. Matt Murphy & Susan Murphy. ISBN 1 870492 75 7

Index of Common Names

Index of Scientific Names

Index of Irish Names